Science on Television

**Science and Philosophy in
Translation Series**

SPTS

Science on Television Bienvenido León

Science on Television.
The Narrative of Scientific Documentary.

Bienvenido León

The Pantaneto Press
Luton

First published 1999 by Ediciones Paidós Ibérica, S.A. *El documental de divulgación científica.*

Published by:
The Pantaneto Press, First Floor, 3 Gordon Street, Luton, Bedfordshire,
LU1 2QP, UK

2007

ISBN 978-0-9549780-1-3

Typesetting: Kerrypress Ltd, Luton

Printed and bound by CPI Antony Rowe, Eastbourne

The Pantaneto Forum
Founded in 2000, *The Pantaneto* Forum is a quarterly journal, which aims to promote debate on how scientists communicate, with particular emphasis on how such communication can be improved through education and a better philosophical understanding of science. The journal is web based and can be found at http://www.pantaneto.co.uk.

To Aurelio and Pilar, my parents. They taught me the first and most important "sciences" in life.

Contents

Acknowledgements

I have been able to compile all the material necessary for this study thanks to the cooperation of many people and institutions. I would like to thank all of them, especially David Attenborough, who always found time despite his busy schedule to help me out. Similarly, Jeffrey Boswall who produces and teaches nature documentaries has been an inspiration for me: his enthusiasm has allowed me to consult documentaries I once deemed as inaccessible.

I must also thank the BBC's Natural History Unit: its head Alistair Fothergill, and its former head, Christopher Parsons. I am also in debt to Sue Lion, director of the Wildscreen competition, Charles Jonkel, president of the *Missoula International Wildlife Film Festival,* and Professor Derek Bousé, at that time of Albion College (Michigan).

The support I have received from the Department of Audiovisual Communication of the University of Navarre and especially professor Jose Luis Orihuela has been crucial throughout this study.

Finally, I would also like to thank professor Juan José García-Noblejas, the director of my doctoral dissertation that served as the basis for this study.

To the Reader

Looking at contemporary television broadcasts, one finds that science is occupying more and more programming space. Scientific knowledge is one of the guiding forces in society's development. It is crucial, therefore, that the average citizen be informed about scientific matters. Yet the language scientists use is quite often difficult to understand for the person who does not form part of that exclusive circle of scientific specialists. That is why it is so important that the broadcasting of this scientific knowledge be made in such a way that it is interesting and easy to understand for the average person.

Despite the difficulty posed when trying to render complex scientific matters into understandable language and images, good scientific programs do exist that serve to bridge the gap between science and television audiences. The documentary as a genre has proven to be effective and has played an important role in the transmission of scientific knowledge in broadcasts. When one looks at television's short history, one can easily find documentary producers who have won the approval of both their colleagues and television audiences, precisely because they have known how to transmit science in an understandable and impressive way.

This study attempts to systematically show the key elements that allow the producer –scientist or journalist- to perform effectively. The theoretical presentation is illustrated by examples taken from the work of noteworthy documentary producers, especially that of David Attenborough, considered one of the best popularisers of our time.

This book has been written to serve as a guide for present and future documentary producers, either as scientists or journalists, who work in the field of broadcasting. The themes dealt with in this study are also of interest to students and scholars of Journalism and Broadcasting.

Introduction

For centuries, scientific knowledge had been the domain of the intellectual elites who quite often found their attempts at transmitting this privileged information futile. Nonetheless, as early as the 17th century, the average citizen began to show interest in scientific matters and social and political motives encouraged the privileged few to spread their knowledge. From that time, scientific knowledge began to search for the means of reaching a generally ignorant audience. The task was not easy and many people actually believed that it was impossible for the average man to understand scientific principles. Others said that only specialists were capable of understanding the different aspects of scientific knowledge and any attempts at explaining and transmitting knowledge would only render it useless.

What is obvious is that scientific knowledge is based on rigorously systematic research that is logically structured, whereas common knowledge is based on a haphazard collection of practical experiences. Thus, when the scientific world attempts to reach a broader spectrum it must breach the gap between these two types of knowledge. The scientist or journalist may attempt to do so through the use of conferences, exhibitions, books, magazines, newspapers or audiovisual means of communication. In the midst of this attempt at communication and transmission a series of questions relating to the nature of the message being broadcast come to the surface. What is specific to this type of discourse? What should this message be like? Is it just the simplification of scientific discourse? Or, on the contrary: are we facing a new type of discourse with its own characteristics?

In addition to these essential questions it is worthwhile considering whether some means of communication are really effective in the transmission of scientific knowledge. Mass media tend to feature scientific issues, which are thought to be of immediate interest for the average audience. What is of immediate interest does not necessarily coincide with what is scientifically important. Many scientists, in fact, feel that mass media are not an effective means of transmission of scientific knowledge. Their sentiment is based on the fact that the working method for scientific research, which is based on an in-depth and systematic line of research, has nothing in common with the working method that characterises the media: immediacy and improvisation.

Furthermore, films and television seem to limit matters because they are a means of communication which use a form of narrative, very different in approach and procedure from that of scientific research. This becomes apparent when one observes the poetic and dramatic way of narrating in any audiovisual medium. Knowledge is not transmitted in a systematic logical way: instead it is presented in an attractive and practical way. What may be strictly intellectual, theoretical or technical is transmitted in an emotionally appealing way.

This study attempts to present some of those key elements necessary in order to effectively broadcast scientific knowledge. In the case of film and television documentaries it strives to present the line of work essential in each context.

In this work I feature certain narrative, dramatic and argumentative techniques, which are characteristics of the work of David Attenborough and other documentary producer's work. Attenborough's contribution to scientific documentaries as producer, writer and presenter has been fundamental in the development of the genre.

The present study situates itself in very fertile terrain that has not been cultivated sufficiently. It is a rich terrain indeed, considering the presence of an inherited, centuries-old, rhetorical and poetical tradition. Yet the terrain has been sparsely cultivated because very little research exists on ways of communicating scientific knowledge. Even less research exists on the use of documentaries as a means of the transmission of scientific knowledge.

Chapter 1   Science Popularisation

The study of effective narrative mechanisms in the popularisation of science through audiovisual discourse has its own place within the general phenomenon of scientific communication. For this reason, it is important to discuss the most common ways of producing such scientific communication along with the most common difficulties involved.

Scientific popularisation is analysed in this study from the point of view that it is a special type of communicative activity, which impartially transmits knowledge that is intentionally shared. In this case, the audience sees science as an objective reference taken from the real world making it, therefore, something free of arguments or point of views. Scientists, of course, have divergent or opposing approaches to the reality they experiment on but the audience, nonetheless, tends to easily accept that a scientific broadcast is unquestionably valid.

1.1   A Historical Approach

It is difficult to determine the exact date on which the scientific world begins to exchange information with the rest of society. Popularisation of scientific matters became possible when there were a sufficient number of people educated and curious enough to take an interest in science. This occurred with the aristocracy and the upper middle class who had the time to cultivate this interest. According to Calvo Hernando (1977: 85–6), the birth of this transmission of scientific matters occurs in the 17th and 18th centuries and it is made possible as a result of the decline of the use of Latin as a *lingua franca* for the educated. Now it was possible for those who did not know this language to learn about scientific matters.

Europe at the end of the 17th century saw the birth of modern science. With this new approach scientists searched for the truth not only because of their love for knowledge but also because of the utility of their discoveries for society. Scientists, with this new vision of knowledge, become allies of the modern state: their discoveries would contribute to improving commerce, industry, health or the craft of war. Seeing its utility, the state was now willing to pay scientists for developing their wisdom. In exchange, they required that these wise men publish the results of their investigations. At this point, many scientific organisations were born, as is the case with the Royal Society in London (founded 1660) and the Academy of Sciences in Paris (founded 1666). This new vision of science, based on mathematical logic, imposed the use of experiments as the sole means of acquiring knowledge about the world. It created a world, which was transmitted in a complex language full of abstract concepts, difficult for anyone who does not know the basic underlying principles to understand at all. A new language became necessary: one that made it easier to transmit the results of scientific experiments to the general public.

The first attempts at transmitting scientific knowledge to a wide audience are made through the use of articles in newspapers and magazines. Throughout the 17th and 18th centuries science becomes a regular presence in the press. The first newspaper to include scientific articles is the *Gazette de France*, founded in 1631 by the French physician Teofrasto Renaudot. This publication informed, on a regular basis, about the different meetings that took place among the scientific communities, some of which occurred at Renaudot's home. These can be considered the first articles that were responsible for the popularisation of scientific matters, because they were aimed at the general public and not at a specialised scientific minority.

The first publications that entirely featured scientific matters appeared a few decades later. The two that are considered pioneers in the field are *Journal des Savants* and *Philosophical Transactions*. The first was founded by Denis de Sallo in 1664 and concentrates primarily on scientific themes, along with literary and philosophical matters. The first issue of *Philosophical Transactions* appears in 1665. In Germany *Acta Eruditorum* first appears in 1682 and is very similar in content to these magazines. In that same span of time similar types of magazines appear in Italy, Switzerland and Holland. Highly specialised scientific newspapers also begin to appear at this time, as is the case with *Nouvelles découvertes dans toutes les parties de la Médecine* that appears in 1679 and is edited by the French surgeon Nicolas Blegny.

In the 17th century science becomes a central theme in a literary genre that becomes popular: famous authors like Diderot and Voltaire contributed to its development. The first significant work in this new genre is *Conversations about the Plurality of the Worlds* (*Entretiens sur la pluralité des mondes*, 1686), where the French writer Bernard de Fontenelle explains cosmology to an imaginary marchioness. In the prologue to this work Fontenelle affirms that his objective in writing is to deal with questions related to the structure and composition of the universe so that the average reader can understand the concepts and the scientific mind can appreciate its depth. This author, thus, poses one of the intrinsic difficulties in publishing scientific matters: accessibility for those who are not experts.

At the end of the 17th century different books are published that deal with science and some of them prove to be successful. These works are basically aimed at the aristocracy, who have the time and money to invest in such works, but they are progressively used in the education of minors. One of the most noteworthy and prolific authors in the 18th century is Voltaire and some of his works are clearly educational, as is the case with *Elements of Newton's Philosophy*. According to Voltaire, science has the right to possess the truth, along with religion and political power. His point of view brought about his own exile yet predicted the role science would take at the end of that same century.

The role of scientists in some countries would prove to be extremely influential. An alliance between the state and science facilitated an opening up to the masses of what had once been reserved to an intellectual elite. Governments began to introduce science as a subject into the educational systems and interest in scientific matters continued to increase. The growing interest of the common people in scientific matters can be seen in the news stories published at that time, dealing with electrostatic energy and magnetism. The invention of the electric battery by Volta in 1800 is a clear example of this type of popularisation.

The French encyclopaedia (*Encyclopédie ou dictionnaire raisonné des sciences, des artes et des métiers, par une société de gens de letters*) is an important work because it was the first compilation and popularisation of scientific knowledge hitherto unknown to most people. D'Alembert and Diderot, who were aided by another 60 authors, among those Rousseau, Voltaire, Montesquieu, Holbach and Buffon, edited the first edition, published in 1780. The work is composed of 35 volumes that offer a compendium of knowledge of diverse sciences, including geography, medicine and zoology. Its purpose is primarily pedagogical and, to achieve it, a simple style is adapted so that explanations are clear and concise – free of any literary mechanisms.

According to Raichvarg and Jacques (1991: 14), the 19th century is the golden age of scientific popularisation. During this century considerable changes occur in the way science is perceived and doubt is cast upon some principles, which had remained unquestioned since ancient times. It is a time of great discoveries based on experimental investigation like those performed for example by Pasteur, Darwin, Rutherford and Curie. In the 19th century science would broaden its domain and simultaneously begin a race towards a specialization of the diverse subjects. As a result, different countries begin to promote science as a part of their plans for development and scientists are rewarded with better facilities for investigation and popularisation of their work. The first scientific publications come into being during this time period and are seen as a means of communication between different investigators. Scientific organizations are also created with the purpose of reinforcing cooperation among diverse specialists in the same field of work.

In the first half of the 19th century the industrial revolution facilitates the popularisation of the results of the scientific investigations occurring at the time. An example of this would be *The Society for the Popularisation of Useful Knowledge*, created in Britain in 1826. The activities these societies undertook are reflected in the news stories published in the press of that period. For example, in the decade of the 1830's the *Athenaeum* regularly published information dealing with the meetings held by the Geological Society of London.

In general, however, the 19th century sees a decline in the number of news stories dealing with scientific matters because political stories become much more popular. Some papers had special sections related to science, while others ran the occasional story informing about the latest results on scientific experimentation. In France, after 1825 the press began to publish brochures that dealt with scientific matters on a weekly basis. Thus the public was kept up-to-date with all the developments of different scientific fields. Specialization became a key word, as scientific magazines began to appear that only dealt with special areas of science. Some of these magazines were extremely pedagogical as was the case with *Scientific American*, founded in 1845 and still published today. When it began to be published, this magazine dedicated many articles to, for example, new machinery, new train routes, the development of commerce and navigation. It also attempted to explain to the general public the principles of physics and chemistry, so as to raise the level of knowledge in general.

The popularity of literature which featured scientific matters continued to increase. One can find very interesting examples of this type of publishing written by Goethe, as is the case with those dedicated to evolution in animals found in the *Annuals of Scientific Criticism* published in 1830. Other authors like Zola believe that science should be separated from literature. Yet most of them use a literary framework in order to make the work attractive. A book whose mission is one of popularisation, according to Arthur Mangin, should attempt to coordinate "one accessory, which is the fictional element that lightens the dialogue and another essential, which is the series of scientific lessons that are the objective of this dialogue." (Raichvarg and Jacques, 1991:111). This genre, which basically used a literary wrapping to present scientific principles, began to decline at the end of the century. It is at this point when science began to form an essential part of the schools' curriculum.

At the end of the 19th century, as a consequence of all the different discoveries being made, science becomes a permanent presence in people's lives. All the different aspects of life that were being affected by these scientific discoveries were constantly in the press. Electricity and all the new materials that had come about as a result of chemical experimentation were now permanent fixtures in the different articles, brochures or other forms of written popularisation available at the time. From this point onwards, scientific popularisation lives some of its greatest moments.

The end of the century sees a growing belief, influenced by positivist and scientific currents of thought, that science could resolve all of mankind's problems. In the shadows of this growing belief were multiple journalistic and literary works that strove to nourish it. The universal world fairs also accomplish a tremendous amount of popularisation, because the inventions resulting from all the different experiments of that period are actually shown to the public, with the hope of generating a future market. Scientists move around their countries, travelling in order to promote their discoveries. The press, of course, covers all of this, aiming at a reader who wants to know how practical and useful all of these things are for everyday life. Scientific matters sell and the press of that period is quite aware of this fact. In 1872, *The New York Tribune* publishes a special edition featuring the lectures on Physics given by John Tyndall, that proves to be a success with 50,000 issues sold.

At the end of the 19th century a substantial change takes place in the relationship between the press and science. From now onwards it will no longer be necessary for the scientist to attempt to popularise his work. Journalists will be the ones looking for the 'scoop': that news story on the experiment or discovery that will have an impact on people's lives. This, of course, is not always possible, since 'scoops' are not typical in everyday scientific investigation. Yet at the beginning of the 20th century this type of news story was essential. The press wanted stories that sold, and any sort of experiment or discovery was rendered in a sensationalist tone. The discovery of radioactivity, by Henri Becquerel, appears in the newspapers of the time as the dream come true of alchemists, and as the promise of happiness in the form of rays.

Some authors establish the birth of scientific journalism at the end of the 1920's, when *The New York Times* begins to publish a series of chronicles written by Waldemar Kaempffert, an engineer who begins to write for this paper on scientific matters in 1927. The fact that writers like Kaempffert with a scientific background were now working for newspapers, helped to undo all the previous damage done by the sensationalist press. This interest to improve the accuracy of scientific information began a few years earlier in New York City, where the businessman Edwin Scripps organizes the first distribution service for scientific news, called *Science Service*. Scripps, the founder of a chain of more than 30 newspapers, believed that the basis of democracy was science. In an age of tremendous sociological and technological change, science was bound to sell. With the help of the renowned zoologist William Ritter and a team of journalists, he organized a service that translated scientific matters into an understandable language for the general reading public. Within a few years the agency had over a hundred newspapers subscribed to its service, making these scientific news stories available to almost 7 million readers.

At this point in time, scientific journalism forms part of all the major newspapers and is actually taught in the universities with journalism programmes. In 1928 Emil Dovifat becomes Chair of the Scientific Journalism and Publicity programme in the university of Berlin. From that moment onwards, he also edits a scientific newspaper published in this academic centre. In the early decades of the 20th century, both scientists and educational experts try to reinforce the educational dimension of science, by establishing a link between the investigators and the general public. Museums dedicated to science are slowly but consistently inaugurated. In Munich the *Deutsches Museum* opened in 1925. In London, a new building housing the *Science Museum* opened in 1928. In Chicago, the *Museum of Science and Industry* opened in 1933 and, in Paris, the *Palace of Discovery* was inaugurated in 1937.

During the years leading up to the World War II and the years immediately afterwards, a new impulse in scientific investigation sets the scene for the technological revolution that takes place in the final thirty years of the 20th century. At this point man can control the atom, has initiated the conquest of space and has substantial knowledge of cellular life. All of these feats continue to interest the public, who now also shows a growing interest in environmental matters. We will later see (section 2.2.2) how this growing interest is an important element in the understanding of the narrative mechanisms used in nature documentaries. Once audio-visual means of communications were developed, most of the efforts in scientific popularisation were channelled towards these new tools. With the appearance of the movie camera, a new research tool was introduced, allowing scientists to film and observe things previously not possible for the human eye to record. At the same time, that which was registered could be shown to an interested public in the form of a film. The scientific community soon saw a new and extremely successful method of popularisation of which we will later speak (section 2.2).

1.2   A Conceptual Approach

Having outlined the historical development of scientific communication, we can now turn to discuss the concept of popularisation. To this end, it is necessary to first establish the notion of science itself.

Although the term *science* has had throughout history and still has today, many meanings, here we shall use the classical definition "knowledge which is certain because of its cause".

In principle, science has a purely cognitive goal as it searches for the truth within itself. Applied science, or technology, uses the same methods as science and various specialised methods, but applies them to ends which are utilitarian and practical. And so science is concerned fundamentally with knowledge, while technology is focused on action or operation.

However, although the intrinsic goal of science is to increase knowledge, there is an undeniable extrinsic goal which is the search for wellbeing and power, even though these may be gained via knowledge. In fact, the birth of modern science in Europe, at the beginning of the 17th century, was motivated as much by the search for knowledge, as by an interest to apply knowledge to diverse areas of life such as commerce, medicine or war.

The fact that science has a primarily cognitive objective imbues it with a series of particular characteristics. Both science and general knowledge aim to give true understanding; that is to say, they try to manifest and give the reason for "the being of things". However, there is a notable difference between the path science takes to the truth and the way used by non-scientific or ordinary knowledge.

For some authors, the difference between scientific knowledge and ordinary knowledge is that the former comprehends "in a

superior way what was previously only partially known, considered or believed" (Fernández del Moral and Ramírez, 1994: 28).
In accordance with this line of reasoning, common knowledge is
based on opinions, which everyday language then assimilates
into beliefs. But, to better understand the meaning of this statement, it is worthwhile pausing for a moment to consider the
significance of the notions used. As described by Llano (1991:
52), certainty is "the state of mind in which one, firmly and
without any fear, adheres to a truth." Certainty is, therefore, not
synonymous with truth, because the former is a subjective state
while the latter refers to the conformity of understanding to
reality. However, certainty in its strictest sense is present when
understanding adheres to a true proposition. The opposite
extreme of certainty is doubt or "the state in which the intellect
fluctuates between the affirmation and denial of a specific proposition, without reaching one extreme any more than the other".
When understanding leans more towards one part of the contra-
diction, this gives rise to opinion: a state motivated by an act of
will and not because the object which is understood claims it
inescapably. In opinions there is no firm ground, but rather there
is an underlying fear of the truth of the alternative proposition.

Because scientific knowledge is based on certainty and general
knowledge on opinions, it seems appropriate to note the considerable distance between the starting points of each. This difference between scientific knowledge and ordinary knowledge has
been observed since Aristotle stated that:

> Argument based on knowledge implies instruction, and there
> are people whom one cannot instruct. Here, then, we must use,
> as our modes of persuasion and argument, notions possessed
> by everybody (Rhetoric, I. 1355 a).

Today, following in the footprints of the Age of Enlightenment,
authors like Calvo Hernando (1977:135) define scientific knowledge as "the set of clear and distinct ideas, on which judgements
are made, in accordance to logic and with the objective of
knowing the truth in a disinterested way". This type of knowledge differs from general knowledge because "the masses live

with vague and confusing ideas, reflect without using logic and uphold a truth in tune with their desires".

Other authors have used similar terms to describe these differences. Guichot (cited in Fernández del Moral and Esteve Ramírez 1994: 27) for example, states that ordinary knowledge is "knowledge which is vague, uncertain, unorganised and without any unification" while scientific knowledge is directed and applied "reflective, certain, systematic and with unification."

Given that the two types of knowledge are built on different foundations and that they use differing methods to access the truth, it is no surprise that the attempt to reconcile the two presents notable difficulties. Science habitually deals with issues that are not easily accessible to those who do not have a minimum degree of knowledge. Furthermore, scientists writing for their peers tend to use a somewhat esoteric style, by which specialists within the same field aim to differentiate themselves from those who do not belong to it. One hundred years ago it was possible for any educated person to understand the meaning of scientific terminology, because it was basically descriptive and based on etymology. Today, however, scientific professional jargon seems to keep knowledge within the boundaries of a small group of professionals.

On the other hand, modern science aims to understand the world using a model of reasoning based primarily on mathematical logic and empirical experimentation. The consequence of this model is that science uses an abstract language which is difficult to understand for those who are not familiar with the basis of this type of reasoning.

The history of science is full of admirable examples of scientist-popularisers (for example: Darwin, Freud, Huxley, Lewis Thomas, Sagan and Jonathan Miller). However, it seems that within the scientific community there is still the idea that popularisation is a difficult task to carry out and of little importance. The relative lack of interest shown by scientists to popularise science is due in large part to the little or no recognition popularizing work receives in the indices of academic success, via the curriculum or professional status of researchers.

Having outlined some of the difficulties which, *a priori*, popularisers encounter, we can now, with a better perspective, turn to the concept of popularisation itself. But, before trying to clarify this notion, it would be useful to focus on the popularizing activity in terms of the three basic elements of any communicative activity: author, recipient and message.

The author of the popularising discourse can be a scientist or a professional in the field of communication. In some countries, it is normal for scientists to popularise science, in other countries this work is normally carried out by specialized journalists.

With regard to the potential recipient, scientific popularisation is directed to the general public, while scientific discourse is aimed at the community of specialists in a particular field. This fact gives rise to the immediate consequence that the popularizing message must adopt narrative forms which can be easily understood by the public, and so may distance itself from the specialist terminology aimed at experts.

As has been mentioned before (section 1.1), the manner in which these messages have been presented throughout history suggests that the recipient is not only interested in knowing the truth of what is being divulged, but also in knowing the meaning that the information may have, and the practical outcomes that can be derived from it, as applied to everyday life.

However, as Thom (1992: 111) points out, science is not characterised by its usefulness or practicality, but rather it places more importance to presenting *aporías* (rational unfeasible proposals) than finding solutions. He puts the birth of science in the paradoxes posed by Zeno of Elea who gave examples showing that scientific knowledge does not necessarily need to be characterised by providing practical solutions, but instead by presenting basic mental experiences of a logical and speculative character.

A first analysis of popularising discourse shows that scientific information is frequently given by way of applications of science, rather than the transmission of knowledge itself. In this way popularizing discourse moves away from science but closer to technology. This distance between the scientific message and popularised message has other features. According to Roqueplo (1983: 139), the popularisation of science favours the assimilation of the discourse used and reinforces the decontextualization of objective knowledge, converting it into "entertainment-discourse". On occasions, scientific popularisation has reached a point where it has little or no bearing on science at all, given that the populariser "dramatizes" the discourse, in order to maintain audience interest, to the degree that it loses its original scientific meaning.

Roqueplo adds that popularising discourse differs notably from scientific discourse, because it is "a-practical" and "unilateral". Discourse is a-practical because the audience cannot carry out any effective validation, which means that they can only interpret the discourse which is presented, as if it were a discourse of reality itself. That is to say, the audience does not normally have the means to verify the information supplied, and must accept it submissively as a valid reflection of reality.

The unilateral nature of communicative discourse is imposed upon it by the nature of the means it uses, such as the press, radio, television, cinema and publications. Roqueplo states that the audience can choose not to receive the message, but it cannot simultaneously receive and exercise a critical stance over it. Thus the gulf which separates scientific knowledge and popularised science is established.

Contrary to what these differences suggest, it is not possible to closely identify popularised science with general knowledge, as the scientific information is part of its own sphere of science and uses its own methods, which do not necessarily coincide with those of general knowledge. In agreement with Brajnovic (1979: 50–51), information can have as an objective the transmission of knowledge which in some cases is more general in nature and in others more scientific. There are also numerous cases which can be considered to be an intermediate situation. However, the information itself has its own scientific field that cannot be reduced to the study of the messages themselves, but to a series of phenomena associated with the communication process. It is precisely through the journalistic presentation of facts that a bridge can be established between scientific knowledge and general knowledge. As Fernández del Moral and Ramírez (1994: 27) point out, specialised journalistic information should start to bridge the traditionally wide gap between scientific knowledge and ordinary knowledge.

Up to this point we have seen some of the characteristics which are common to all types of popularizing discourse, focusing on the author, recipient, and the message itself. However, not all popularizing discourse is aimed at the same audience, nor does it use the same means of transmission. On the contrary, it is important to distinguish different levels of popularisation. Some authors establish these levels according to the greater or lesser proximity of the scientific message to the popularised discourse. Rudolf Flesh (1960: 79–84) establishes three levels of popularisation. The first is that which focuses on the results of research, and only communicates those aspects that may be of use to the audience, following a model analogous to that of an electrical appliance instruction manual. Discourse at the second level communicates the meaning of the research in question and discusses how the discovery was made. The third level, aimed at the scientific community, goes one step further and offers a scientific explanation of the facts which are presented.

For other authors (see Calvo Hernando, 1977: 105), the levels of popularisation are directly related to the means by which the message reaches its audience. In this type of classification scheme, the first level corresponds to rapid communication, usually by means of radio and television, and is of immediate interest here. It holds audience interest but does not offer in-depth coverage of topics and, on occasions, lacks the necessary scientific rigor. The second level is the one which carries out a more mediated and complete type of popularisation, which is generally carried out via specialist magazines, scientific sections in newspapers, conferences or other similar media. It differs from the first in that there is a more in-depth approach to topics.

Fernández del Moral and Esteve Ramírez (1994: 127–128) categorize popularisation according to the degree of communication between scientists and the general public. This communication is generally carried out on a daily basis: either through the press or on the radio or television. They put forward two levels of specialised communication, called intermediate and specialised. At an intermediate level the scientific elite establishes links with a mass audience, normally through the use of a weekly means of communication. Finally, at a specialised level, a relationship is established between the scientific elite and the cultural elite through specialised magazines and monographs.

This is the criterion which is used in this study, which means that the use of the term popularisation should only be understood with reference to a type of communication whose intended audience is the general public; that is to say, people who lack specialised scientific knowledge, although they are generally, in the widest sense, interested in science.

Keeping these considerations in mind, it seems appropriate to consider the objectives of this study and to define scientific popularisation as a communicative activity which attempts to transmit to the general public knowledge taken from science, through a new type of discourse whose aims and methods are not necessarily scientific. The notion, thus formulated, does not deal with the circles in which this communication takes place. Although some authors consider scientific popularisation to be only that which occurs outside the official educational system, or its equivalent, and which does not form part of a specialist training programme. Others, on the other hand, include certain types of educational and pedagogical discourse as possible forms of popularisation. Fernández Rañada (1995: 159–160) points out that one of the possibilities the populariser has, is to write a manual in which all the necessary concepts are explained in simple terms.

Although a detailed study of the relationships between popularisation and education is not possible in the present study, it is important to note that between the two concepts there is an initial distance. Both educational discourse and popularizing discourse set out not only to redress the simple lack of or need for knowledge, but they try to reduce ignorance, or the absence of knowledge, for which a person has a natural aptitude. However, while education concentrates on transmitting that which it considers essential for a dignified life, popularisation generally focuses on information that is not considered essential, and so it needs to use different ways of communicating to transmit its messages effectively.

The concept of scientific popularisation, as mentioned above, deliberately refers to the non-scientific nature of the objectives and means of popularisation. With respect to the objectives, as has been previously noted, the objective of the populariser is not necessarily the transmission of knowledge itself. With respect to the forms used, popularisation uses certain resources which constitute a specific type of discourse, by which it is possible to establish the necessary bridge between scientific and general knowledge, in such a way that the public becomes interested in science and is able to understand it.

The distance which separates popularised discourse and scientific discourse has been discussed by Roqueplo (1983: 114) who states, "the populariser is more a creator than a translator". In the case of popularizing using audiovisual means this distance is even greater. To begin with, science uses, fundamentally, the written record, which is particularly appropriate to transmit ideas, which have been logically structured. Furthermore, as Silverstone (1986: 81) points out, television is aimed at everyday experiences, which further complicates its relationship with science.

According to this author, television programs dealing with scientific matters carry out a mediating role between discourse which is "specialised and general, written and oral, empirical and phenomenological, (…) ultimately, between science and common sense".

The question of the form of non-scientific popularizing discourse is especially important in this work, which focuses on the study of the narrative means used in science documentaries. Establishing the radical difference between scientific and everyday types of discourse allows for an analysis of which forms the mediation between the two areas of knowledge use, through a series of resources or techniques.

1.3 A Sociological Approach

Having established the concept of scientific popularisation and outlined the discourse used to transmit science to society, we shall now turn our attention to the role popularisation plays within the framework of social communication.

In the 20th century science became ever more specialized and complex. Furthermore, scientific knowledge multiplied to such a degree that no single person was able to assimilate everything. Not even the communication technologies of the time, in spite of providing the means for a greater freedom of circulation of information, were able to help a general public who had physical access to scientific information, but not the means to understand it.

A high degree of specialisation, in turn, reduces and hinders communication between specialists from different fields and, above all, between scientists and society in general. In this way, although science plays an important role in the debates which mark the developmental path of a society, the lack of effective communication between scientists and the rest of the community makes the relationships between the parties all the more difficult. This lack of communication not only affects the general public,

but also, as García-Noblejas (1996: 219–20) points out, constitutes the greatest challenge facing modern science today. According to this author, in the situation we have at present of excessive
specialisation, scientists are unable to present their findings in the
context of general knowledge, and so they are of interest to only
a small group of experts in the field.

When the public is unaware of scientific and technological issues
this can affect the political basis on which society rests. The
political function of the popularisation of science was of particular importance in society at the beginning of the 21st century,
when science and technology had an ever more notorious presence in the lives of many people. In this context, there are
increasingly numerous and significant political decisions in
which science has a key role.

Only in a society where genuine popularisation exists, is it
possible to foment an intelligent debate on issues over which
citizens have the right to decide directly or indirectly. Furthermore, society pays attention to science not only because it seeks
knowledge for its own sake, but also because it is aware that
knowledge can help meet certain needs. The popularisation of
science, therefore, is especially relevant as the element which can
restructure the life of a person, and lessen the growing inability
of man to adapt to a world strongly impregnated with science and
technology.

Calvo Hernando (1992: 31–32) suggests that scientific journalists
have three functions in society. The first is to inform and to
stimulate the curiosity of the public, to heighten its sensitivity
and moral responsibility. Second, they act as interpreters, clarifying the meaning and significance of scientific discoveries, especially those that most directly affect daily life. And finally,
scientific journalists carry out a certain control on behalf of the
public, so that scientific developments are considered in political
decision-making.

On the other hand the popularisation of science is necessary not
only because it brings science to the general public, but also

because it supports education and brings all fields of science up to date. In this way popularisation becomes a useful tool for scientists who can use it to face the growing complexity and breadth of science and keep themselves up to date.

As Jiménez Aleixandre (1995:45–48) has pointed out, it should be remembered that a large part of learning takes place through "informal" means; that is to say, outside the established channels such as schools. Popularisation, therefore, plays a decisive role in the knowledge people acquire about various subjects, especially in those where the "formal" channels do not pay sufficient attention. Moreover, popularisation is a means of awakening among the young the notion of the role played by researchers in society.

All of the above highlights the gap between popularisation and teaching, which becomes more evident if we consider, together with Choza (1982: 15), that education forms part of the process of what is termed "primary socialization", by which the individual acquires basic knowledge about the world and society.

However, as García-Noblejas (1988: 45–46) has shown, the media themselves at times act as instruments of primary socialization, because they tend to present lifestyles that offer "objectivities (…) of the image of man and they way he acts in the world." The author goes on to say that it is in this way that the period of primary socialization, which was once reserved for the periods of infancy and adolescence, now remains indefinitely open, and audiovisual media "seem at times to be real schools of illiterate scholars".

Despite the importance of popularisation within social communication, when working, the populariser is faced with a series of difficulties that stem from the social relationships that arise from the nature of the work itself. Scientific discourse, and to a lesser extent the popularised form of science, are usually surrounded by an aura of mystery, which itself is based on the idea of inaccessibility to science for the great majority of the public. The popularisation of science contributes to foment this feeling of inaccessibility when it convinces us that we shall never be able to understand science, thus creating a "show-case" effect. According to Roqueplo (1983: 127) this effect is as follows:

> The popularisation of science "shows" us science, it enables us to see its actors and its products; but at the same time it convinces us that we shall never be rich enough to actually buy those products and it puts scientists behind the glass showcase, in an inaccessible place.

The message that is being popularised also transmits, implicitly, a certain fear of scientists, because it considers them as having special, almost limitless, knowledge. Popularisation transmits a series of myths about science, which contribute to the idea that the world is constantly penetrated by sacred forces. In this context, the public come to regard the populariser as a priest who mediates between scientists and normal people.

On the one hand the means of social communication frequently diminish the quota of information in order to, little by little, introduce spectacle and entertainment. Journalism focuses generally on spectacular and unusual events, which awaken the interest of society at a particular moment in time. On the other hand, science rarely has reasons to violently interrupt this panorama of current affairs which circulate in the means of communication. Furthermore, the journalist tends to work tremendously fast, whereas the scientist aims to ensure accuracy, and thus works at a more measured pace.

Faced with such a situation, some popularisers resort to narrative structures that distort the meaning of the scientific information, highlighting secondary issues which, nevertheless, attract audience interest. This dramatisation of science becomes more evident when using audiovisual media, where the demands of staging are clearer.

In spite of the difficulties presented by making staging requirements and scientific accuracy compatible, there is no reason to initially relinquish a balance between the two. In this regard, the following statement by Bettetini (1995: 29) is particularly appropriate.

> To make a program that truly popularises science, which is really a vehicle for the communication of research, and which at the same time takes into consideration the demands of the audience: it is not always possible, but it is possible (…) The problem arises when there is a move from the compatibility of the scientific objective to the demands of spectacle and the subordination of one to the other.

The situation described above points to the need to establish solid bridges between science and general knowledge, encouraging a popularisation that is capable of making the demands of journalism compatible with that of science. In this way it will also be possible for the average person to be well informed in matters of science, so that they will be able to better understand the world in which they live.

It is in this framework that the study of the popularisation of science through audiovisual discourse should be placed, and more specifically, the analysis of the narrative mechanisms of the scientific documentary. As we shall see in chapter 4, these documentaries constitute a model of popularisation based on solid scientific approaches, centred on the fundamental issues within a given scientific discipline. But in addition to this, they constitute a model of popularisation that is capable of presenting information in an intelligible and interesting way to the general public. But, before entering into an analysis of these models, it is necessary to deal with the language employed in the popularisation of science.

1.4   The Language of Popularisation and its Characteristics
The study of the peculiarities of the language used in popularisation, as carried out in this work, is based on the consideration of some of the features highlighted by the study of different types of language use – scientific, literary and journalistic. Using these

features as a starting point, the characteristic features of the language used in the popularisation of science are then analysed.

Given that scientific knowledge is of great interest to society, the language it uses should be inter-subjective, in the sense that the content can be exchanged between different members of a community. The ideal of contemporary scientific language, especially in natural science, is found in mathematics, which expresses results concisely and unequivocally. For this reason, any ornate element is eliminated, the aim being to achieve the maximum possible brevity and precision. Bulhoff (1992: 29) dates the origin of this tendency to the beginning of the 17th century at the start of the domination of the empirical method which clashed violently with Aristotelian principles, particularly those with regard to science and its associated rhetoric.

The ideal of empirical science, which was held by Descartes, Locke and Kant and is still held by many today, states that there is an objective truth which scientists can find and express by means of a transparent language. For this reason, scientists consider language to be an instrument which allows them to reveal reality precisely and unequivocally.

However, as modern physics has shown, the very process of observation by scientists produces a distortion of reality. Furthermore, the work of certain authors has revealed the fallacy which underlies this ideal of empirical scientific language. Roland Barthes (1994: 25), among others, has referred to the problem of considering language as a mere instrument of thought, given that "man does not pre-exist language, philologically or ontogenetically speaking". However, despite such objections, there is still a tendency today to ignore the mediating role that language plays in science, especially in natural science.

Up to a point, popularisation maintains this univocal and clear approach that characterises scientific language, even though the language of popularisation is different to that of science. As mentioned above, one of the most notorious differences is its use of non-scientific language, such as dramatic mythological structures.

Furthermore, the scientific text has a more anonymous character, as the author does not form part of the wording, and has the same status as other authors mentioned above (section 1.3). On the other hand, in the language of popularisation all quotes and critical references are eliminated and substituted by the notorious presence of the author, whose credibility is a sufficient guarantee for the audience. In some cases the language of audiovisual popularisation includes contributions by other experts who, to a degree, have a similar role as critical references in a scientific text. However, in other types of popularisation the narrator is perceived to be the sole reference point.

Diametrically opposed to scientific language, which is supposedly unequivocal and transparent, is literary language, whose aim is to create an aesthetic experience. The literary historian Roman Ingarden points out that, in contrast to the scientific text, the aim of a literary work is the work itself, because the pleasure gained from reading is its primary objective. According to Ingarden (1968: 151), the aesthetic experience of a literary text is made the more satisfying the greater the richness of meaning and subjective interpretations it offers.

This aesthetic goal leads literary language to habitually employ rhetorical techniques which, in principal, appear to be inappropriate in the context of scientific language. This last point can be accepted as a general consideration, although the fact that many noteworthy scientists have used abundant rhetorical techniques should be taken into account. Einstein, for example, frequently used visual icons to communicate his theories and Darwin was a master at using metaphor. According to Gould (1992: 59), not only did Darwin use metaphor to communicate his ideas, but he also used metaphor in the genesis itself of his theories, and in the search for the knowledge preceding their formulation.

A third type of language, clearly differentiated from scientific and literary language is the language of journalism. In principle, the language used in popularisation is similar to that found in

journalism, given that it is very often journalists who are responsible for popularisation, and this takes place within the context of
social means of communication.

But I hasten to say that, as Martínez Albertos (1989: 149–50)
points out, it is difficult to consider journalistic language as
something unique. Martínez Albertos classifies journalistic languages according to the means of communication used for
transmission (written text, radio broadcast, television broadcast
and cinema) and according to the approach used (information
dissemination, interpretation and commentary).

Martínez Albertos (1992:185–203) considers popularisation to be
an activity that lies outside the sphere of journalistic approach.
However, in among the features he mentions as being those
which characterise journalistic language, can be found some
which are also common to the language of popularisation.

In some ways, the language of journalism seeks, as does literary
language, to awaken in the audience a subjective feeling. To
paraphrase Nelkin (1990: 166), the journalistic text "chooses its
words depending on the wealth of their evocations". However,
beyond this evocative statement is that of Lázaro Carreter (1980:
159–60), who claims that journalistic language has a "non-
literal" quality; that is to say, that it should be considered
according solely to its content and by its "pieces and joints".

Lázaro Carreter (1977: 11–12) also points out other characteristics that separate literary language from journalistic language.
One of these is that, while the reader of a literary work is not
guided by utilitarian needs, the reader of the press does seek to
fulfil this type of need. This utilitarian aspect is, however, less
important in journalistic language than in other types of language
which are more highly specialized.

However, journalistic texts of popularisation do have a pragmatic
aspect, because there is a tendency to leave aside hard science in
order to focus on the practical applications, or on the repercussions the scientific issues may have on the audience.

On the other hand, even though this "non-literary" feature is a primary characteristic of journalistic language, it is clear that some journalistic genres do have an aesthetic quality. Television programs that focus on information dissemination, documentaries in particular, have an extremely important aesthetic component which is apparent, above all, in the search for beautiful images and a balanced composition. These audiovisual broadcasts are often produced in such a way that the most beautiful or striking images are highlighted as much as possible. The fact that images are eye catching or artful even plays a decisive role in the choice of a subject matter.

The language of popularisation, therefore, especially in the audiovisual context, acquires a concern for language itself, be it verbal or visual. However, it is also clear that this concern for form does not eclipse the basic aim of popularisation, which is to transmit science. Using Aristotelian terminology we face an "apophantic logos", where what is fundamental is what tells the truth or lies; rather than a "poetic logos", where truth is secondary to realism; or a "pragmatic logos", where language is used in a practical way with daily concerns in mind.

In the light of the above, the language of popularisation can be identified as a specific type of journalistic language that also shares some features of scientific language and that, frequently, shows concern for the aesthetics of the discourse itself.

According to Calvo Hernando (1992: 91–92), the expression of scientific and technological issues poses a series of specific problems. First of all, experts in the field of popularisation and journalists in general, often lack the necessary scientific terminology. This problem is compounded in the case of the coverage of science. Second, the inherent complexity of scientific language, from which stems the need for its popularisation, means that the process of creating an effective message is not easy. Finally, the necessary specialization of science contributes to a more obscure language. To this should also be added the desire of some scientists for a secretive approach to their work.

In order to overcome these obstacles, the language of popularisation should pay particular attention to certain aspects which, although present in other contexts, here acquire special relevance in the popularisation of science. Of these aspects, there are two which are especially important: clarity and precision.

Aristotle (Rhetoric, III 1404) refers to clarity as one of the necessary virtues for any speech to have its desired effect. He goes on to say that, for this to be clear, the style used in the speech should not be "either below or above what is necessary, but appropriate". Clarity is recognised as one of the key elements to establish appropriate scientific communication, whether or not it is to be popularised. As recommended in a style manual aimed at biologists and medical doctors (Herranz, 1993: 68–9), clarity in an expository style is necessarily preceded by clarity of thought and this is based on conciseness, precision, and good organization.

With regard to the means of achieving clarity, some authors, like Fernández del Moral and Esteve Ramírez (1994: 28), have established formulae to create an index of legibility. This legibility index is understood to be "the aptitude of a text to be read, understood, and memorised as quickly as possible". In order to determine this index, various formulas have been proposed, such as those by Gary-Leary, Cloze, and Flesch. In general, they all try to measure the degree of difficulty of the discourse by counting, for example, the number of difficult words or the length of the words or phrases.

On the other hand, Nuñez Ladeveze (1991: 151) believes that clarity is not a quantifiable issue but rather a question of style, both literary and humanistic. He also points out that clarity is not obtained at the price of simplifying the message carrying the information, or by losing the density of the content. It is more a question of adapting the content to a "standard average bench-mark" level. As a result, for any text to be clear it should respect the linguistic norms that allow it to be understood; that is to say, it should be grammatically correct. Nuñez Ladeveze also points out that the clarity of the language of popularisation means that in addition to following grammatical rules, it should avoid superfluous technical language and use non-technical, everyday language.

In the discourse of popularisation, the adaptation of language to a standard average benchmark, which implies the use of everyday language, avoiding for example, unnecessary technical terminology, is particularly important. Calvo Hernando (1977: 196) states that effective popularisation should avoid terminology from scientific jargon and mathematical formulae as these discourage the reader. However, there are occasions when the use of technical terms is necessary, as they allow for a more in-depth approach to science. For this reason, in some cases, it can be extremely complicated to express certain concepts without using technical language. On such occasions a sensibly cautious approach to communication recommends giving an explanation of all those terms which may be new to the audience.

Similarly, the use of formulae is staunchly defended by some scientists, as it is the only means of expressing certain ideas. Without dismissing the fact that this indeed may be the case in some situations, it is important to note the example given by the Nobel Prize winner Richard Feynman, one of the creators of quantum electrodynamics. His book *QED: The Strange Theory of Light and Manner* is a good example of how complex theories can be clearly put forward without having to revert to one single mathematical formula or to reasoning which is inaccessible to the general public (see Martín Pereda 1995: 16).

In the case of audiovisual popularisation, which shall be discussed (chapters 3 and 4), the need for clarity also affects the way in which the images and sounds are presented, as well as the relationship of these with any verbal information or commentary, which may be given.

A second essential quality of a good popularisation discourse is precision. From the perspective of clarity, language is always interpretative, as it always implies a judgement of speech. Consequently, it is not possible to establish an absolute, unequivocal relationship between language and object. However, in general terms, we can state that a language community that is able to understand the meaning of a text acquires, via the language of the discourse used, an understanding of the objects referred to.

In general, a precise language is that which makes reference to an object in an unequivocal way. The first and most important source of precision is the adjustment between language and object, from a semantic point of view. Given that every word has its own nuances it is difficult to find two synonyms that are exactly alike in meaning. That is why it is necessary to choose, in each case, the term that designates most explicitly and unequivocally the object which is referred to. If this is not the case, if the relationship between language and the object is not unequivocal, the text becomes ambiguous and confusing.

As is often the case, this language-object relationship becomes clearer when specific terms are used instead of abstract ones, because the object which is referred to is open to fewer different interpretations. In general, when using the language of popularisation, it is recommended that the specific term be used instead of the abstract one, as the absence of the specific makes it more difficult for the audience to assimilate the issues raised.

Semantic precision poses particular problems for popularisers, because sometimes their lack of in-depth knowledge of the subject matter produces unavoidable inaccuracies.

In addition to inaccurate semantics, ambiguity may come from the use of complex or incorrect syntax. Precision is better achieved through short sentences which avoid levels of subordination. It is also preferable to avoid discourse which is "full of conjunctions and relative pronouns that blur or confuse relationships and that could lead to divergent interpretations" (Herranz, 1993: 74).

The use of anaphoric references (terms that repeat the meaning of a word in the same phrase or paragraph) can lead to inaccuracies.

It is for this reason that scientific language avoids reference markers such as relative pronouns, although this means paying the price of repeating some terms. On the other hand, the language of popularisation, as found in different means of communication, tends to avoid the repetition of terms and often uses anaphoric references, placing more importance on the agility of the text, to the detriment of accuracy.

With regard to the implications of precision in audiovisual broadcasting, it is important to consider, firstly, that in the cinema and on television there is a marked preference for specific terms rather than for abstract ones. This is the result of the fact that the images generally shown are themselves specific objects. In view of this fact, it has been suggested that the words which accompany the images should also use specific terms.

First and foremost, then, audiovisual means of communication have an enormous capacity to refer with precision to a scientific object because they have at their disposal the help of the visual image. However, science also needs to express abstract ideas which have to be expressed in the discourse, but where images may actually be a hindrance. This difficulty has been highlighted by professionals in the field of scientific journalism, who have openly said that television and cinema are not the ideal means of communicating abstract scientific ideas.

However, it is important not to forget that audiovisual discourse does enable abstract topics to be dealt with, by using various narrative approaches. The first consists of using the narrator's voice to explain in more general terms what the images show in a specific manner. It is also worthwhile remembering that both in the cinema and on television the juxtaposition of various images can create meanings that go beyond the literal meaning of each one of the shots. Finally, a synthesised image, created by a computer, also offers the possibility of creating a visual support, which is appropriate to tackle abstract issues.

However, the fact that audiovisual discourse can deal with abstract topics does not mean that this is the best medium for this purpose. On the other hand, a written text can be used to express certain ideas, in such a way that they can be understood more easily. For this reason one of the difficulties faced by those who popularise, using audiovisual means, is precisely to gain the maximum benefit from the potential of the medium and to look for narrative forms which help to compensate for its shortcomings.

Chapter 2   The Film and Television Documentary as a Means of Scientific Popularisation

Looking back at the path taken by the historical development of scientific popularisation, we can see that both cinema and television have been used as a means to popularise science. In among the range of audiovisual narrative forms used by popularisers, such as, for example, drama, daily news and documentaries, there is one which is especially noteworthy: documentary.

Of the different subjects which general science documentaries deal with, there are two which particularly stand out: anthropology and nature. The historical development of these two types of documentary will be discussed in the following sections. But, before doing so, the notion of what constitutes a documentary should first be clarified.

2.1   An Approximation to the Concept of a Documentary

Throughout the history of cinema and television, the term *documentary* has been applied to work of various types and characteristics, such as newsreels, educational films, travel films, and television programmes of different styles and content. Because the concept of a documentary is difficult to define, a historical overview of the different uses of the term can be useful in order to clarify its meaning.

The English word *documentary* was used for the first time by John Grierson (who started the British documentary movement), with reference to a film, by Robert Flaherty. In 1926 in his review of the film *Moana* by Robert Flaherty, published in *The New York Sun,* Grierson (1966: 11) wrote: "Being a visual account of the daily life of a Polynesian youth, and his family, (...) it has documentary value".

Based on later writings by Grierson, it can be deduced that the term *documentary* is an adaptation of the French word *documentaire,* which was already used in the 20's to refer to films dealing with travel.

Etymologically speaking, *documentary* comes from the root *document* which in turn comes from the Latin *documentum;* from which arises many of the generic meanings of the word in modern day English.

In the context of cinematographic language, the *Oxford English Dictionary* defines *documentary* as follows: "Based on facts, realistic; specifically referring to a film or literary work, etc. Based on real events or circumstances and with the primary objective of education or registration of facts".

Other definitions of the term have been formulated, over the years, by noteworthy documentary producers. Paul Rotha (1970: 65), British producer and director, wrote in 1932 that the documentary was synonymous to "a film with a specific interest in scientific, cultural, or sociological topics"

On the other hand, John Grierson (1966: 35–36) believes that films of a scientific or educational nature are not strictly speaking documentaries. Although he does recognise that films, which use material taken from reality are generally grouped under this heading, he suggests that this category be reserved for those that include some kind of significant artistic contribution. Grierson (1966: 40) understands a documentary to be the "creative treatment of reality" and believes that it would be appropriate to establish the formal limits of the different "species" of documentaries.

According to Grierson, within the different works subscribed to the genre there are different ways and approaches to observing reality and organizing the material on which it is based. It is therefore important to define the concept precisely. Using this approach, Grierson (1966: 36–37) establishes three main guidelines for the documentary. First, he believes that documentary cinema is "a new art form, full of life" (…) that can "photograph living scenes and the living history". The second guideline states that characters and scenes taken from reality offer better possibilities to interpret the modern world. Finally, Grierson believes that the material taken from the world should be able to reflect the essence of reality, capturing spontaneous gestures and emphasizing movement.

Various authors have tried to draw the line which separates the documentary from other audiovisual categories, which take reality as their objective. Logically, it is very difficult to precisely define the line encompassing the vast panorama of works produced by various artists, at different historical periods and using differing techniques.

In some cases the defining criteria which is used is the declared intention with which the work was carried out. According to Barsam (1974: 3), the documentary differentiates itself from the broadest category of non-fiction films, because of its socio-political objective. While the "non-fiction film" category includes all those works that deal with historical events, he suggests calling documentaries only those works that have a message and are considered to be works of art. Barsam believes that a documentary is capable of influencing society. Therefore, for documentary makers, cinema is usually something more than fun or a combination of education and entertainment.

Purpose is also the main criteria in the definition by Paul Rotha (1970: 5), for whom the documentary is "the use of cinematographic medium in order to creatively interpret reality and, in social terms, the life of people as they are in reality".

The North American director and producer Phillip Dunne (1946: 176) also defines the documentary according to its purpose, stating that the documentary is nearly always, in its widest sense, "an instrument for propaganda", for which reason it is considered to be an 'idea-weapon created to strike a blow in favour of the cause the author has in mind". From this definition it follows that the documentary can deal with issues taken from reality or from the author's imagination. It may, therefore, have a plot or not, and, as a result, could even use actors in the production.

It is common to differentiate between documentaries and current affairs programmes. Barsam (1974: 3) notes that the documentary is to a current-affairs programme what an editorial is to the pages of a daily newspaper; the editorial is based on the opinion of the media, while the news is based on fact.

Although this criteria of objectivity can at times be enlightening, it should not be forgotten that, within journalistic audiovisual genres, there are some, such as the chronicle or the report, that have a strong subjective component, without their generally being referred to as documentaries. Generally speaking the distinction between a report and a documentary is based on how current is the theme being dealt with, which implies certain methods of production. Although there are noteworthy exceptions, documentaries are normally produced using a script, whereas current affairs reports focus on recent events or on events that occur during filming. In any case, as Pancorbo (1986:13) points out, sometimes "a good report is similar to a documentary and certain documentaries are like television films, which, often, seem like extracts of the news".

It is not easy, therefore, to define precisely the term documentary, from the analysis of differences with other audiovisual genres based on real events. Moreover, in some cases it is not even easy to determine if a work is fictional or non-fictional. How does one classify, for example, works that use actors to represent real situations?

As Nichols (1991: 27) states, one of the fundamental expectations of the viewer of a documentary is that the sounds and images which make it up, be a true reflection of the real world. That is to say that, as an audience, we believe that what happens in front of the camera has not been substantially modified during the recording and subsequent editing process.

This definition would exclude those broadcasts whose starting and reference point is not reality itself. Also excluded are those which do not interpret what happens in the world, but rather limit themselves to present a mere transcription of real events, for example, certain news items or reports.

This viewpoint also allows us to consider that the documentary usually presents knowledge that is freely shared, whereas the news reports tends to focus on questions that are subject to controversy. Furthermore, the documentary has a vocation to communicate permanent knowledge or knowledge that will last, at least, for a considerable length of time. On the other hand, a news report deals with current information which, by its nature, is transient.

This important criterion also appears in the definition put forward in 1948 by the *World Union of Documentary*. According to this institution, a documentary is "all methods of registering on celluloid any aspect of reality, interpreted either through the filming of events or through the true and justified reconstruction of events appealing to reason or to emotion, with the objective of stimulating interest and broadening human knowledge and under- standing, in order to earnestly consider problems and solutions in the fields of economics, culture, and human relations".

2.2   The Science Documentary

It is not easy to draw the boundaries around the area which defines the popular science documentary, given that the term 'science' refers to numerous disciplines and is open to various interpretations. Furthermore, all human knowledge is related in some way to a scientific discipline, and so other types of documentaries could also be considered as popularisations of subjects derived from science. On the other hand, the use of a documentary, as a means of popularizing science goes hand in hand with the use of scientific films as a means of research, used by scientists. The dividing line between the two is consequently difficult to see.

Nonetheless, there are some cases where the relationship between the content of a documentary and certain aspects of science is clear. In certain cases, it is because the audiovisual media develop topics which constitute the object of a specific study of some scientific discipline. And in other cases, it is because the documentary includes images and sounds that have been used by researchers as tools of study, and therefore help the audience understand more clearly specific natural phenomena. It is in this context that the following section will deal with some noteworthy contributions made over the years.

Since it started, film has found in science one of its most remarkable motifs. The organisation of images and sounds is as much an instrument that aids scientists, as it is a medium to disseminate their findings, via documentaries and other popular-izing programmes. The moving image is used by scientists as a research tool, as it makes it possible to show certain phenomena which are imperceptible to the human eye. Film can record that which is for our own natural perception, too small, too big, too fast or too slow. In this way, with the help of audiovisual means, a scientist can have access to a more detailed understanding of reality.

Even before the appearance of the film by the Lumiére brothers, some scientists had performed experiments, which had allowed them to record some moving images. The French astronomer Pierre Jules Cesar Janssen developed a recording system called the "revolver cinematographique", which consisted of a cylinder-shaped camera with a revolving photographic plate. Thanks to his invention, Janssen was able to record, in 1874, the transit of Venus as it passed between the earth and the sun.

One of the first scientific fields to use film was medicine. Already in 1896, in Russia, film was used to document certain surgical techniques. There are also accounts that in Poland, Boleslaw Matuszewski, a former film operator, filmed various surgical operations, from 1897. Matuszewski thought that film could be extremely useful and recommended its use in a range of activities including art, science, defence and education. In 1898, scientists from various European countries made films on a range of medical topics; for example, one was about the movements of partially paralysed patients, filmed in a Bucharest hospital. In Great Britain films of medical topics were also made in the first few years. The pioneer of medical film, in England, was Dr. Parchen who, in 1898, produced three films on different diseases.

The first notable attempt to use film as a means of popularizing science was made by the British company Urban Trading, founded by Charles Urban. In 1900 this company showed, in a London theatre, the film *Invisible World,* produced by Martin Duncan, featuring microphotographs for public viewing. Later, this same company would produce other notable works of popularisation, also using microscopic images. These works would later form a series called *Unseen World*, in which there were films such as *The Circulation of Blood in the Frog's Foot* (1903).

Other outstanding productions in the first years of the 20th century are those by the French producer Jean Comandon on *Microscopic Life in a Pond* (*La vie microscopique dans un étang, 1903*), and by the Italian producer R. Omega, on the different phases of metamorphosis of a butterfly, made in 1904.

From then on, popularizing scientific films began to appear as short films that preceded full-length fictional films in cinemas. The majority of these scientific films dealt with topics related to human science, especially in the form of travel films. Other frequently used themes were the natural sciences.

During the two World Wars, scientific film underwent a notable development. The French magazine *Sciences et Voyages,* at the time, regularly ran a scientific film review section. In these reviews it can clearly be seen that this type of film was already using, to great effect, educational and dramatic techniques which contributed to the popularisation of science. It was during this period that the use of film as a scientific instrument, and as a means of popularizing science, spread throughout the world. In the United States there was notable experimental work, for example, in 1924, Dr. G.R. Ganti managed to film a culture of organic tissue.

In Great Britain various initiatives of scientific film production were developed. One of the most outstanding was undertaken by the Shell Film Unit. A report by John Grierson for the oil company lead to the creation of this film unit, that produced outstanding films based on scientific and technological content. By the end of the 1930's this unit had established subsidiary production centres and archives in many countries. The Shell Film Unit was active until 1954, fulfilling its goal which was to make the company renowned for its leading role in the fields of science and technology. Among the most notable scientific films, which it produced, there are two which deal with the use of insecticides: *Atomization,* 1949, and *The Rival World,* 1954. The latter captures man's struggle against insects, in different countries.

Animation provides numerous possibilities for scientific films and popularizing scientific media. One of the first experiences in this field was that of Emile Cohl, who in 1908 produced *Happy Microbes.* At the beginning of the 1920's the company Atlantic Films produced a series of short films called *Three Minutes.* This series included films such as *Three Minutes of Astronomy,* in which the movements of the moon and the planets are accelerated. These series were recognised as good examples of scientific film, because of their ingenuity and tremendous ability to disseminate knowledge to the general public. The reviews of the time highlighted, because of its mastery of the use of popularisation techniques, one episode from the same series called *Commotion in Combat* (*Branle-Bas de Combat* 1934), about a French warship.

As Raichvarg and Jacques (1991: 188) point out, the use of animation in scientific films gives rise to different opinions. The magazine *Sciences et Voyages* noted that, although much had been published about Einstein's theory of space and time, animation did much to help the public understand its importance. On the other hand, Jean Painlevé believed that cartoons were a medium which was too pedagogical and could not replace the documentary, as a means of scientific film.

The use of sound in films opened new horizons for scientific film. On the one hand, narration opened new possibilities and meant that it was no longer necessary for conferences and exhibitions to be completed by commentaries *in situ*. Furthermore, music became an extremely important narrative element. However, some reviews of the period already pointed out that, in some cases, the commentary was useless or had taken a mistaken approach.

During World War II, in some countries, the production of scientific documentaries was limited or totally suspended. In other countries, on the other hand, quite outstanding initiatives were undertaken. For example, the British Ministry of Information produced films like *Scabies* (1943), that attempted to instruct doctors on the diagnosis and treatment of this skin disease. Other medical documentaries produced by this same ministry were: *Blood Transfusion* (1942), about the national blood transfusion service; and *Penicillin* (1944), about the new antibiotic.

Once the war had ended, the National Film Board in Canada produced various documentaries, among which those dealing with mental health stand out. The series *Mental Mechanisms,* directed by Robert Anderson, dealt with various mental illnesses such as *The Feeling of Rejection* (1947), *The Feeling of Hostility* (1948), *Over-dependency* (1949) and *Feelings of Depression* (1950).

Scientific documentaries received a considerable boost as television became more popular. Of the many programmes made over nearly half a century, two of them stand out. Both pro-grammes have produced magnificent documentaries on many different scientific topics and have achieved the most important international awards. One of them is *Horizon*, broadcast on the BBC from 1964 until today, which is widely recognised as one of the world leaders in this field. Another international reference is the series *Nova*, produced by the US public television channel PBS, since 1973. One of the programmes in this series, which had most impact, was *The Plutonium Connection* (1975), about the dangers of using this metal. Another outstanding episode of *Nova* was *Incident at Brown's Ferry* (1977), based on the nuclear accident which occurred in a nuclear power station in Alabama.

According to the British scientist Danah Zohar (1995: 19–13) the majority of audiovisual scientific programmes can be put into three categories. The first is made up of those programmes that present scientific facts directly, generally through statements made by the scientists themselves, which the audience does not usually understand. In the second category are those programmes that present a sensationalist and pessimistic view of scientific discoveries: for example, nuclear accidents or genetic manipula-tion. The third type of programme focuses on strange and peculiar topics in order to surprise the audience. Faced with these erroneous approaches, Zohar calls for the need for quality pro-grammes, where science is placed within reach of the audience.

There are many different topics which the popular scientific documentary deals with, but there are two in particular which stand out: anthropology and nature. These will be the subjects of the following sections.

2.2.1   The Anthropological Documentary

Even when documentary films were first produced, audiences were fascinated by images of landscapes and peoples from remote parts of the world. This interest spurred the rapid devel-opment of a style of documentaries focussing on an anthropo-logical content.

Precursors to these documentaries were the very first films, showing scenes of everyday life in various countries. In March 1895 the public in Paris watched, in awe, the first documentary in history: *The Lumière Factory workers Leave to Go Home* (*La sortie des Usines*). A few months later film operators from this organization travelled all over the world filming and showing documentaries that lasted approximately one minute.

A few years earlier, the Lumière brothers in Europe and Thomas Edison in North America had developed the first equipment capable of recording moving images. In contrast to the system designed by Edison (the kinetoscope), the Lumière cinematograph was much lighter (barely five kilos) and could be easily carried outside to film on location. Furthermore, the cinematograph could be converted into a projector by making some small adjustments.

Amongst the first films by Lumière are *The Arrival of the Bullfighters* (*Arrivée des Toréadors*) filmed in Spain; *The Coronation of Nicholas II* (*Couronement du Tzar*), filmed in Russia; and *The Melbourne races* (*Les Courses*), filmed in Australia, all made in 1896.

In the following years other companies from other countries followed Lumière's steps and began to produce films that they called *documentaries, news programmes* or *travelogues.* Many of them followed the style of showing the audiences exotic peoples and places. From then on, and during the first decade of the following century, the number of films showing expeditions with, more or less, an anthropological or ethnographic focus mushroomed. Two of the first ethnographic films are *Eagle Dance* and *Wand Dance*, filmed by one of Edison's operators in 1898.

During the first years of cinema, the majority of the films produced and shown were documentaries. But, towards the end of the first decade of the century, fiction began to dominate the screens. In this period of decline, films dealing with expeditions made up one of the few styles of documentaries which was still of interest to audiences. Two interesting examples are the productions filmed during the expedition to Alaska by the Carnegie museum in 1909, and by the British producer Herbert Ponting on captain Scott's expedition to Antarctica (*With Scott in the Antarctic*, 1913). Another noteworthy production in this same style was made, in 1914, by the North American ethnologist Edward S. Curtis on the lives of the Kwaiutl Indians in the North West Pacific: *In the Land of Head-hunters*.

This interest was due, basically, to the fact that these films showed exotic peoples and places. The exotic continues to be a key feature of documentaries. It has been so throughout its history, and exotic elements can be seen both in films of an anthropological focus and those which deal with nature. An exotic setting forms an essential aspect of the work of one of the most outstanding producers, not only when dealing with anthropological issues, but with the history of documentary filming. The producer in question is Robert Flaherty, often called "the father of the documentary".

Flaherty began filming to supplement his work as an explorer. However, filming soon became a passion to which he would dedicate his entire life. Throughout his career he made numerous contributions to the development of documentaries, both from the point of view of structure and narrative elements used, and from the production of his films. Some of his contributions have had a special influence in the later development of general scientific documentaries.

His first work, *Nanook of the North* (1922), centres on the actions of one character, in contrast to what was considered normal in travel documentaries of the time, which followed a simple organizational scheme. Flaherty converted the daily life of the hunter Nanook into the main thread around which the entire documentary was woven.

Nanook of the North, considered to be the first masterpiece of documentary film, presents the conflict of a man trying to survive in a hostile environment. This struggle between the protagonist and nature becomes a dramatic element of great importance and constitutes one of Flaherty's greatest contributions to the genre. In other works, such as *Man of Aran* (*1934*), Flaherty also presents another similar conflict, in this case, the fight between man and the sea.

The same theme of the relationship between man and nature also appears in other important works of his career, such as *Moana* (1926) and *Louisiana Story* (1948). Flaherty, who was fascinated by man in his natural state and by the craftwork of primitive man, considered technology to be a dehumanzing threat. According to Ellis (1989: 25–6), underlying this choice of primitive cultures, there is an attempt to consolidate the very essence of the human condition. On this subject, Flaherty's wife wrote:

"Robert Flaherty loved primitive peoples, he loved their simplicity and their dignity, and the way they were free to be themselves. He loved the tremendous courage and generosity he found in Eskimo life".

Flaherty showed great sensitivity when he dealt with the problems presented by man's relationship with nature. Although his works showed exotic places, one of his key characteristics was his focus on the daily life of ordinary people, which was not common in the films at the time. The originality of his approach, explains why he had serious problems finding a distributor for his film. Nonetheless, from its premiere, it was well accepted by the public.

According to Ellis (1989: 17), the success of Nanook was due to the fact that the viewer could see "ordinary people doing ordinary everyday things – working, eating, sleeping, travelling, playing with their children, etc.- behaving in front of the camera as if it wasn't there." This approach to the everyday, of which Flaherty is a forerunner, now constitutes one of the techniques used in documentaries to bring the topics closer to the audience. As we will see later (section 3.1.1), proximity, whether it is physical or conceptual, is a decisive element when engaging the audience in the topic. Some documentaries present as pressing issues, points which are initially far removed from the sphere of interest of the audience, in order to highlight those aspects which are in fact closer.

From the point of view of production and filming, Flaherty is also considered to be a great innovator, even in his first film, *Nanook,* he used techniques that, at the time, were only used in fiction. Among these, one that stands out is the deconstruction of a sequence into multiple shots, so that the audience can see the action from different angles and distances. In order to carry out the deconstruction of an image, Flaherty reconstructed reality in a way that best suited filming. To do this he placed the characters in the best possible place and even made people who appear in the film do things just so that they could be filmed. As Barsam (1988: 20) notes, Flaherty justified this reconstruction of reality saying "Sometimes you have to lie. Very often you have to distort something in order to capture its true spirit".

This type of production allowed sequences to include moments of suspense; a dramatic technique, as will be seen later, that has since been used in other documentaries. Furthermore, the fact that the actions were presented according to the director's interests also meant that the visual narration was extraordinarily simple and clear: elements which are especially effective in scientific documentaries.

Dramatic reconstruction is particularly evident in *Elephant Boy* (1937), a film which after shooting many scenes on location, had to be completed in a studio. Some critics of the period considered this film to be an example in which the dramatic elements were too contrived, so that it could not properly be considered to be a true documentary. These same reviews pointed out that, although dramatic elements may be useful to bring science closer to the public, if these elements then completely overwhelm the work, then the work is no longer a documentary, but has become pure fiction.

After *Moana,* Flaherty frequently used telephoto lenses, which allowed him to record images otherwise unattainable, and to allow characters to act more naturally. At the same time, Flaherty (1934) discovered that the use of telephoto lenses endowed the images "with a stereoscopic quality and a brilliant, beautiful realism." The telephoto lens was an indispensable element in the filming of nature documentaries because it was the only way to capture a large number of wildlife scenes. Furthermore, the use of telephoto lenses added to the heightening of the beauty of the images, in the way described by Flaherty.

For John Grierson (in Barsam, 1988:57), Flaherty was one of the great innovators in the history of cinema, because he was the first to consider the camera as "an eye with which to observe with more precision than normal vision allows". Although a school or movement was never created by or around Flaherty, his influence on other documentary makers was and continues to be very significant.

The style of anthropological documentaries developed greatly after the premiere of *Nanook.* This approach, which at first was initially developed in North America, continued to deal with man's relationship with nature. Among the most important films of those years were the ones made by Merian Cooper and Ernest Schoedsack, films by Martin and Osa Johnson, and those by the French producer Leon Poirier.

Among the first films on travel, are the North American productions: *Hunting, Big Game in Africa* (1923), by H.A. Snow; *Wild Beauty* (1927), by H. McRae; and *With Byrd at the South Pole* (1930), by Admiral Byrd.

The first documentary by Cooper and Schoedsack, called *Grass* (1925), was released successfully by Paramount. The film showed the migration of 50,000 members of the Bakhtiari tribe in Persia, in search for pasture for their sheep. Of note in the film was a spectacular scene in which the members of the tribe crossed the torrential river Karum, with the loss of many lives. In

1927 the same team filmed *Chang*, in Thailand, which focussed on the struggle of a family to survive in the jungle. After this start in the field of documentary film making, the team formed by Cooper and Schoedsack went on to produce some fictional films, achieving their greatest success, several years later, with *King Kong* (1933).

The husband and wife team, Martin and Osa Johnson, produced various films based on their own expeditions, including: *Congorilla* (1929), *Wonders of the Congo* (1931), *Baboona* (1935) and *Borneo* (1937). These works have been criticised for focusing mainly on the self-glorification of the producers, who were constantly in shot showing their bravery and for portraying a negative image of African peoples.

The French producer Leon Poirier made *The Black Cruise* (*La Croisiere Noirie,* 1926); a film subsidised by the company Citroen, about a car journey like no other, crossing Africa from North to South and reaching the French colony of Madagascar.

In the years that followed, the production of anthropological documentaries continued, until the start of World War II, when the production was interrupted. After the war, this approach to documentaries made a good recovery, thanks to the work of, for example, the French producer Jean Rouch. His first films dealt with life in Africa: *The Hunt of the Hippopotamus* (*Chasse a l'hippopotame,* 1946) *Cemetery in the Crags* (*Cimétiere dans la falaise,* 1951) and *The Men that Make Rain* (*Les Hommes qui font la pluie,* 1951). Years later, Rouch worked from the Musée de l'Homme, in Paris, where he promoted the production of various films with anthropological themes. His work *Chronicle of a Summer* (*Chronique d'un Eté,* 1960) is considered to be the start of the movement called "cinema verité".

In the United States, anthropological films of the same period were given a boost mainly by Gregory Bateson and Margaret Mead. Their films *Trance and Dance in Bali, Childhood Rivalry in Bali and New Guinea* appeared in 1952. Other noteworthy anthropological documentaries produced at the time in North America were *The Hunters* (1958), by John Marshall, and *Dead Birds* (1963), by John Gardner.

When television began to offer the documentary a new framework for its development, the production of anthropological documentaries multiplied, transforming it into one of the most established and widespread types of documentary. Despite this diversity, the narrative forms used by precursors, especially Flaherty, are still valid today.

2.2.2   The Nature documentary
One of the most common themes found in scientific documentaries is nature. According to Bousé (2000: 44), the first film to show wildlife was *The Sea Lions' Home*, filmed in 1898 by Edison. The 25-ft film shows sea lions entering and leaving the water.

However, even before the appearance of film by the Lumiére brothers, experiments had been carried out to register the movements of animals. Around 1875, the Englishman Eadweard Muybridge made various attempts to photograph the movements of racehorses. These experiments, which were financed by a racehorse breeder, were carried out by placing a number of photographic cameras along the path taken by the horse. In this way it was possible to reproduce the complete process of the gallop. Following on from this, Muybridge experimented with filming sequences such as a tiger attacking a buffalo; which was the first recorded instance of animal attack set up expressly for the purpose of filming. These films were the start of a trend for nature documentaries to be made in controlled conditions, a trend which would continue to be dominant in North America for various decades.

The French psychologist Etienne Jules Marey, a follower of the work of Muybridge, tried, rather unsuccessfully, to film bird flight. He later applied the technique to other animals, and managed to obtain two or three second sequences which showed, for example, a cat falling from a height. It is in these experiences that the origin of another concept of a nature documentary can be found, a concept that would become a strong basis for documentary traditions as, for example, in the UK. What was implicit in Marey's approach was the aim to record the movement of animals in their natural habitat in such a way that the presence of film crew did not change their behaviour in any way. These two films set precedents for nature documentaries, because in them were the seeds of the two main lines of production that would be developed in the following decades.

a)   The European Tradition
During the first years of cinema, many films were shot in gardens, in which, insects or spiders, for example, would appear. There were also many films of birds, generally in their nests, a theme that would in later years take up many metres of celluloid. These images, when projected onto a large screen, were well received by the audience.

From those early years there were also films whose aim was to record images of scientific interest. One of the pioneers of the use of cinema in zoology was the Englishman Alfred Hodden, who in 1898 participated in an expedition, from the University of Cambridge to the Torres Strait, and took with him a Lumiére camera.

In those years some British producers were already making films about animals. One of the oldest preserved films was made in 1900 by G.A. Smith and showed a spider making its web. Other pioneers of British nature films were Oliver Pike and the brothers Richard and Cherry Kearton. Pike was the producer of the film *In Birdland* (1907), considered to be the first important work of this nature which was shown in Europe.

In the first part of the 20th century, the newsreels in cinemas frequently included images of animals filmed in the wild or in captivity. Some of the companies responsible for these short documentaries also produced longer nature films, often for educational purposes. The company Pathé produced, in 1921, what is considered to be the first conservationist film: *What's left of Bison Herds.*

One company which stood out from all those producing educational films was Gaumont British Instructional Films, founded in 1913. This company produced two nature series: *Secrets of Nature* and *Secrets of Life*, which were very successful with the public. These series had the collaboration of scientists such as Julian Huxley and Humphrey Hewer and producers such as Bruce Wolfe and Percy Smith. Gaumont British Instructional Films, at one point, had the largest archives of educational films in the world.

Over the years, in various European countries, there was an increase in the production of nature films. In addition to the above-mentioned British producers, one of the first which stood out in this field was the French biologist Jean Painlevé. His early works were experiments filming underwater life, in which he used techniques such as high speed, slow motion, and time-lapse photography, that would later be widely used in other nature films. His films were also exceptional because of the excellent lighting work. Painlevé carried out all of experiments not just with scientific rigor but with also with the aim to create works of art in which the surrealism present in nature would be perceptible. His first works date back to 1928: *The Octopus* (*Le pieuvre*), *Stickleback Eggs* (*Oeufs d' Epinoche*), and *Sea Urchin Les* (*oursins*). His most famous work was *The Sea Horse* (*L'Hippocampe,* 1934), for which Darius Milhaud composed the accompanying music. This film was classified (Raichvarg and Jacques 1991: 191) as "a major work, given that spectacle as seen and felt becomes pure enchantment". Painlevé later produced other films based on the lives of famous French scientists such as Paul Langevin, Jean Perrin, Louis Lumière and Louis de Broglie.

In the 1930's most zoological studies no longer only focused on taxonomical work, as in earlier years, but now mainly dealt with trying to explain the behaviour of living beings. In this context, the cinema became an instrument of great interest for scientists and there was an increase in film production. In Germany the production company UFA created a scientific film division, directed by Dr. Ulrich Schultz. Among the films produced by this division the following two stand out: *In Bird Paradise* (1935) and *The Strength of Plants* (1935). In the latter, time-lapse photography was used to speed up plant movements so that they could be perceived by the human eye. On the use of this technique, film critics of the period wrote (in Raichvarg y Jacques, 1991: 187): "The extraordinary awe felt by the viewer is due to the fact that the cinema now seems to be a magical, miraculous instrument, thanks to which are revealed the most profound mysteries of nature".

In the 1930's the production of this type of documentary was already well developed in Great Britain. One of the most famous documentaries of the decade was *The Private Life of the Gannets* (1934). This film succeeded in bringing together the talents of John Grierson and Julian Huxley and was shown in British schools until well into the 1950's.

During the same period there were other noteworthy productions which were made under the seal of the company *Strand Zoological Production,* a department of the production company *Strand Film Company,* which was concerned with animal films and was directed by Paul Rotha in its first two years (1935–37). This company produced films about animal life such as *Free to Roam,* produced by Stuart Legg in 1939.

The start of World War II interrupted the production of nature programs as non-official assignments for production companies disappeared, for which reason many had to close down. In spite of this, some producers did manage to complete nature films. The Frenchman Georges Rouquier directed *Farrebique,* produced during the War and released in 1946. In this film there were sequences of a variety of insects, reptiles, and plants. In some, Roquier used time-lapse photography to be able to accelerate the movement of organisms that would otherwise appear to be inert.

During this period the Swedish producer Arne Sucksdorf also made films based on nature and animal life. During the War he produced various short films, the most outstanding of which were: *August Rhapsody* (*Agustirapsodi,* 1940), *This Earth is Full of Life* (*Din Tillvarosland,* 1941), and *A Summer Story* (*Sommarsaga,* 1941). All of these films included various sequences of animal life filmed with mastery. His first full length feature film was *The Great Adventure* (*Der Stora Aventyret,* 1953), which took two years to make, based on the relationship between a young man and various animals, among which were an otter and a fox. In his films, Sucksdorf combined images of wild animals with others of animals he himself had tamed. In this way, he was able to obtain spectacular action sequences, such as that of the capture of a dormouse by an owl, which appeared in *The Great Adventure.*

The years immediately following World War II, saw the start of the first national organisations dedicated to promoting this type of cinema, such as The Society for the Production of Natural History films, created in England in 1946, and the International Association of Scientific Cinema, founded in 1947. At the time, the production of nature films was slowly beginning to recover.

In the early 1950's, the BBC began to produce its first television nature programmes, establishing the bases for a style of production that made it a pioneer not only in Europe but worldwide. Following the approach taken during those years, the first programmes about animals were filmed live, the majority from the BBC television studios. George Cansdale, superintendent of the London Zoo, presented a weekly program that became very popular, in which he took animals to the studio. These first programmes had very little footage as, above all, the film itself was expensive, given the resources available at the time.

Soon, other nature programs were being produced from Bristol, where there were naturalists who already had experience working in radio broadcasts. In this group was Peter Scott, producer of the first nature documentary which was broadcast by the BBC: *Wild Geese (1953).* Another noteworthy BBC collaborator in those early years was the German producer Heinz Sielmann, whose film *Woodpeckers* was aired in 1955. This documentary included impressive footage of these birds in their nests and was considered (Boswall, 1968) to be "a masterpiece of cinematographic technique, that set the standards for the coming years".

Very quickly, nature programmes began to appear on a regular basis on the BBC. The first series, called *Look,* by Peter Scott, would be aired from 1954 to 1956 and included not only films made by collaborators but also films made by the BBC itself. Among the most noteworthy collaborators were the Belgian explorer and film producer and his wife: Armand and Michaela Denis, who from the 1930's onwards, had been producing films on animal life in Africa. The couple arrived in London from Kenya in order to show their documentary *Below the Sahara* (1954). With the extra footage from this film they were able to produce a half-hour television program, called *Filming Wild Animals,* which showed different species, such as elephants and lions in their natural habitat. The program was well received and the BBC management decided to produce other programmes following similar formats. Another couple were the German naturalists and divers Hans and Lotte Hass whose series *Diving to Adventure* appeared on the BBC in 1956.

1954 also saw the first documentaries by one of the most outstanding nature documentary producers, David Attenborough. His first series, *Zooquest,* continued to be aired for over a decade, and brought to the British public animal wildlife from all over the world. The quality of the technical production and the narrative techniques used in *Zooquest* became a reference point for many other programmes produced in later years. Furthermore, as a result of the series, Attenborough became a well-known figure among British viewers.

In 1964, at the height of his career as producer and presenter, he was appointed to a managerial position in the BBC, first as controller of BBC2 and then as Director of Television Programming. In 1972 he resigned in order to return to programme production, beginning a phase where he wrote and presented some of the most outstanding documentary series in the history of scientific broadcasting. His most notable works are: *Life on Earth* (1979), *The Living Planet* (1984), *The Trials of Life* (1990), *Life in the Freezer* (1993), *The Private Life of Plants* (1995), *The Life of Birds* (1998), *State of the Planet* (2000), *The Blue Planet* (2001), *The Life of Mammals* (2002), *Life in the Undergrowth* (2005) and *Planet Earth* (2006). In all of these documentary series, Attenborough manifests an extraordinary capacity to transmit scientific knowledge to the general public, in a way which is rigorous, entertaining and accessible.

In 1957 the BBC created the Natural History Unit (NHU), based in Bristol, which soon became a reference point worldwide for the production of this type of documentary. From the very beginning, its programmes were characterized by the scientific rigour of their content and by the constant technological innovations used in their production.

At the beginning of the 1960's the naturalist Gerald Durrell began to collaborate with the NHU. His collaboration with the Bristol unit first produced the series *Two in the Bush* (1962), filmed in Australia, New Zealand and Malaysia. He later produced other series for television, of which the following stand out: *The Amateur Naturalist* (1983), *Durrell in Russia* (1986) and *Ourselves and Other Animals* (1987). Durrell was also well known for his literary works and his extensive work as a conservationist.

One of the most important series produced by the NHU in the sixties was *Life in the animal world*, broadcasted fortnightly from 1965, alternating with *Horizon*. This programme, presented by Desmond Morris, included studio discussions among outstanding international scientific experts on animal behaviour.

From 1961 the BBC was faced with a serious rival, as ITV began to broadcast *Survival*, produced by the company Anglia Television. This series is one of the longest-running series in the history of nature documentaries and a worldwide reference within its genre.

Another outstanding work, whose success continues to today, is that of the French naturalist and producer Jacques-Yves Cousteau. His first short films about underwater life were *At Eighteen Metres Depth* (*Par dix-huit métres de fond,* 1943) and *Shipwrecks* (*Épaves,* 1945). His first international success came with his first full-length feature film: *The World of Silence* (*Le monde du silence,* 1956). Later Cousteau would achieve more success with other works, like *The World Without the Sun* ((*Le monde sans soleil* 1965), *The World of Jacques Cousteau* (*Experience precontinent III,* 1965 and *Voyage to the End of the Earth* (*Voyage au bout du monde* 1975). In addition to these films, Cousteau was also responsible for the production of a number of television documentaries.

For more than half a century he carried out numerous exploration expeditions on land and in the sea the world over. His work produced documentaries which were broadcast by television channels all over the world, and which are today the symbol and prototype of the most exciting enviormental audiovisual programming. According to one of his biographers (Madsen, 1989: xiii), "hundreds of millions of people, thanks to his films and television programmes, have learnt about the oceans and the importance and beauty of nature."

In Spain, there is outstanding work by Félix Rodríguez de la Fuente, who is considered to be the most important populariser of the fauna and flora of this country. His first films were *Lords of the Space* (*Señores del espacio,* 1963) and *Wings and Claws* (*Alas y garras,* 1965). In 1964 he began to collaborate with the Spanish television programme *Weekend* (*Fin de semana*) in a short section dedicated to hunting and fishing. His first television documentaries were made in 1966, the year he went on two expeditions to Africa, where he made five programs for the series *Full page* (*A toda plana*). Part of this footage was later reused in the series *Adventure* which he directed from 1969 to 1970.

His most extensive series was *Blue Planet* (*Planeta azul*), of which 153 episodes were broadcast (1970–73). He later went on to direct and present the work that made him internationally recognised: *Man and The Earth* (*El hombre y la Tierra,* 1974–1980). This series was divided into two phases: the first based on the fauna in South America and the second on the fauna in the Iberian Peninsula. Félix Rodríguez de la Fuente was killed, along with two members of his team, in a plane crash in 1980, while filming footage for a new series based on Canadian fauna. Since his death, Spanish production of nature documentaries has been limited.

In the last few decades, there has been an increase, all over Europe, in the production of nature documentaries. This increase was spurred on by the environmental and conservationist movements which developed in the 70's and 80's. These movements have contributed to the growing presence of this type of content in the programme listings of general television channels, both public and private, and specialised channels. The proliferation of the latter all over the world is due in great part, to the inclusion of nature documentaries in the programming.

Over the last few years, public television channels have continued, in most countries, to programme and produce, more frequently, this type of documentary. At the head of these state channels which produce extremely high quality nature documentaries, continues to be the BBC. Other public broadcasters which also maintain a stable, high quality production are, for example: ZDF (Germany) and ORF (Austria). Recently, some private channels have increased their production of nature documentaries, using them as an alternative to drama programmes, even at peak hours.

b)   The North American Tradition
According to Bousé (1997:3), the experiments Muybridge carried out, in 1884, in the Philadelphia Zoo, set the scene for a new way of understanding the nature documentary in the United States. In these types of documentaries, there is an emphasis on spectacular images and dramatic situations, even though, to obtain these images, it is necessary to bring animals face to face in controlled

settings. In this category can be placed a film made in 1903 by Thomas Edison that filmed the electrocution of a circus elephant on Coney Island, near New York.

In the first decades of the century, the most popular films in the United States were about safaris. One of the most successful was *Hunting, Big Game in Africa* (1909) by Coronel Selig, which was shot in the United States and included footage of a lion in captivity, filmed under controlled conditions. Another very successful film was *African Hunt* (1912), which was shown in New York City movie theatres for the extraordinarily long period of fifteen months.

Some followers of the anthropological approach developed by Flaherty, included in their work scenes of animal life. *Chang* (*1927*) by Merian Cooper and Ernest Schoedsack, showed a family's struggle to survive in the jungle of Thailand, surrounded by tigers, leopards and elephants. Later they produced *Rango* (1931), based on the life of an orang-utan, a film which is considered to be one of the first full-length films on animal life. In 1929, *Congorilla* by Martin and Osa Johnson included, for the first time ever, recordings of animal sounds. A few years later the North American Frank Buck participated in expeditions to capture wild animals in Africa, which were recorded in films such as *Bring 'em Back Alive* (1932), *Wild Cargo* (1934) and *Fang and Claw* (1935). During these years there were also films that were made for the express purpose of popularizing science, a noteworthy example being the series *The struggle for Life* by Stacey Woodard.

During World War II, some movie newsreels set aside a permanent section for this type of subject matter, such as the very short section on animal life, with commentary by Lew Lehr, which was shown in North American cinemas. In Canada, the National Film Board produced some nature films, a notable example of which was *High Over the Borders* (1943), based on the migratory patterns of birds.

After World War II, there appeared in the genre of nature films one of the cinema makers whose contribution was considered to be the most decisive by some and, by others, the most damaging: Walt Disney. In 1948 Disney produced his first nature film, the short film *Seal Island,* filmed in Alaska. When the film was finished, it was rejected by the large distributors. Finally it was shown in a movie theatre in Pasadena and later won an Oscar for the best short film. Following this experience, Disney decided to establish his own distribution company, Buena Vista, convinced that there was a public interest in films about animals. From then on he made other short nature films, such as: *Beaver Valley* (1950), *Nature's Half Acre* (1951), *Water Birds* (1952), and *Bear Country* (1953). All of these also won awards from the North American Academy of film, for the best short film. A large part of these films was made using footage bought from independent producers of educational films. The main contribution to this series that he made was, for the first time, to bring the animal world to a mass audience.

In 1953 Disney showed his first full-length nature film called *The Living Desert,* which was followed, one year later, by *The Vanishing Prairie.* Both won awards from the Hollywood Academy and were extremely successful at the box office worldwide. These films were the first to adapt to nature films, techniques normally used by the Hollywood studios in fictional productions, such as simultaneous filming with different cameras, close-ups, and organised and repeated takes of a scene depending on the needs of the film. Even then, these films were made in large indoor spaces, using tame animals and staging fights between them. From the 1960's Disney continued producing nature film with similar techniques.

Despite their success, biologists and naturalists fiercely criticised these films because of their lack of scientific rigor, which could clearly be seen, for example, in the extreme anthropomorphism to which animal life was subjected. In some sequences animals were portrayed as human parodies, using to this effect specific editing techniques and music to create a burlesque affect.

According to Bousé (1995: 35), in the world created by Disney the frontiers between reality and fiction disappeared, as his films with real animals replicated the same narrative techniques he used in his animated films. The controversy surrounding these films can be better understood if we consider with Jonkel (1985: 105) that the Disney films, by using animals as actors, created in the public a false understanding of the animal world.

> The typical Disney film uses animals as if they were part of a cast, with a narrator speaking in the place of the animals. In this way, wild animals are used as actors or puppets. This is exploitation, which is often extremely harmful because people are given false information which later negatively affects the management of wildlife and the countryside, legislation and the relationship between man and animals.

The nature films which were produced in North America until the beginning of the 1970's were clearly influenced by Disney's films. In general, their objective was mere entertainment, they often lacked scientific rigor and, in some cases, it was difficult to even classify them as documentaries.

1963 saw the debut of the North American television series *Wild Kingdom* which quickly became one of the longest-running series in the history of American television. Its presenter, Marlin Perkins, became a well-known personality, whose conservation efforts had a great influence in North American society. These programmes aimed to include a scientific viewpoint, which was missing from the Disney films. However, the majority of the scenes were filmed with captive animals.

From 1975, the production of television nature documentaries received a notable boost due to the introduction of new legis-lation to promote the prime time broadcasting of documentaries. The new documentary trend which was then established differed notably from the style created by Disney, given that, in the new productions, advising scientists took on a major role, one similar to that already found in other documentary approaches, such as the British. In this context, some production companies under-took programmes with high budgets, which allowed film crews to be sent to remote places, for long periods of time and with considerable technical and human resources.

Within this new approach of documentary production, stands out the television unit of the *National Geographic Society*, which had begun to produce nature films in 1961. The *National Geographic* documentaries paved the way for this new trend, showing that when there is financial investment, scientific programmes can be as interesting as the biologists believed they would be. The large investments which were made allowed for the production of programmes which were truly spectacular, showing images of extraordinary technical quality.

These programmes created enormous interest in the general public, mainly due to the fact that they had such stunning images. Furthermore, they kept a good balance between scientific rigour and entertaining narrative techniques. Over the years, *National Geographic* has become one of the world leaders in the production of nature programmes.

Of the productions made in the United States in the past decades, there is one series that stands out: *Wild America*, the first episode was broadcast by PBS (Public Broadcasting Service) in 1981. Its producer and presenter, Marty Stoufer is today a popular personality on American television.

Chapter Three   Narrative and Dramatic Techniques

As with any other activity of a practical nature, the science documentary can be studied from different perspectives, as it includes aesthetic, poetic, ethical, political and rhetorical considerations. This study focuses only on a rhetorical analysis, in the hope that this approach constitutes one of the means to understand, even only if in part, the key building blocks used to produce effective programmes which can then bring science closer to the general public, through audiovisual media.

This type of discourse uses a series of techniques, i.e. a set of procedures and resources which help to achieve a style of communication that is effective. The aim of the following sections is to analyse the techniques used in these types of documentaries and to explain how these resources contribute to the dissemination of certain aspects of science.

When analysing these documentaries, three types of techniques can be considered: narrative, dramatic, and rhetorical. The first supports the narrative and is used by the narrator. Dramatic techniques are found in the representation of direct action, without the mediation of a narrator. Finally, rhetorical techniques try to explain the way in which these documentaries aim to convince the viewer.

Rhetorical analysis could be included within the other two categories, given that, in fact, it is not a set of different techniques, but instead offers a different viewpoint to the others.

Because, as has been mentioned above, this study adopts a rhetorical perspective, all the techniques which are analysed are likely to be viewed in the light of rhetorical doctrine. However, it was considered preferable to maintain the distinction between the three types of techniques as this allows for a more accurate dissection of these types of documentaries, and therefore a deeper understanding of the mechanisms used in the popularisation of scientific knowledge.

The first two categories, narrative and dramatic techniques, can be said to have a more direct link with poetic discourse, whereas rhetorical techniques correspond more specifically to a rhetorical dimension. Therefore, the first two types can be grouped together in a common category, as they are techniques which are aimed at poetic interest, in contrast to rhetorical techniques which try to give the discourse a style of expository reasoning.

Within poetic techniques, the distinction between narrative and drama was first made by Aristotle (*Poetica*, 1448 a), who considered two modes of representing reality:

> With the same means it is possible to imitate the same things, sometimes narrating them (already converting oneself into someone else to a certain extent, as Homer does, as oneself and without changing), or presenting all the imitators as operators and actors.

As pointed out by Genette (1989: 221), this Aristotelian division reappeared at the end of the 19th century with the distinction between *showing* and *telling* formulated by Henry James and his followers, and which then became a guiding principle in British and American novel writing.

From the Aristotelian distinction it follows that the difference between narrative and dramatic techniques is that the latter aim to imitate reality, with a seemingly apparent absence of a centralised discourse which acts a mediator between reality and the audience. In this case, the characters behave as if in reality itself. However, as Muñoz Torres (1996: 157) skilfully argues, narration and drama have in fact an enunciation capacity, which in the one case is visible and in the other not; although, in drama the audience tends to forget that someone has previously selected the events that are presented. With respect to science documentaries, as we shall see later, a particular combination of narrative and dramatic forms is used with the aim of presenting to the audience a faithful rendering of reality.

The aim of the narrative, dramatic and argumentative resources that are used is to make the audience interested in the programme and to help them understand it. For this reason, some of the techniques used have the common feature of trying to bring the facts and ideas that they wish to communicate closer to the sphere of interest of the audience.

3.1 Reaching out to the audience's interests

At this point it is worthwhile pausing to analyse some of the key aspects of interest to the general public in scientific information. With regard to scientific communication, the audience can approach the discourse with different motives. Roqueplo (1983: 87–88) makes the following distinctions:

1. A real desire to understand "what it's about" or "how it works". However, it seems that this curiosity is not strong enough to become a "will to learn".
2. An attempt to acquire a cultural code that can establish social position: this is, in fact, a means of social promotion.
3. A need to "orientate one's life". "What meaning it can have for me, to orientate my life".
4. An interest which focuses on the problems of origin: the origin of the world (cosmogony), of the Earth, of man in general, of the individual, etc.

Even though these may be the reasons why the general public listens to, watches and reads scientific broadcasts and publications, the media do not always respond to these expectations. According to García-Noblejas (1900: 46), the media associate what is interesting with what is useful and, in this way, highlight superficiality, because the truths which are closest to the roots of mankind, such as philosophical and religious truths, cannot be easily approached or dealt with.

Muñoz Torres (1991: 205–207) expresses a similar concern when he discusses the exemplary effect of the media. The media, because it gives examples of behaviour, acts as a reference point when taking decisions. According to Muñoz, capturing the interest of the public means trying to make the public feel involved in what is being communicated. Therefore, actions become more interesting the more they affect life.

These approaches seem to explain the fact that the public is often not interested in science itself, but in its applications and in the way in which scientific discoveries can affect their lives. So it is not surprising that some broadcasters and publishers believe that, in general, people are interested in that which affects their way of life, from an everyday point of view.

However, to better understand why the audience is drawn to the communicative discourse, it would be advisable to pause, although only briefly, to consider the concept of "news value". According to Muñoz Torres, (1996: 249).

> News value (...) can be described as that quality belonging to journalistic discourse that produces in the reader or viewer a certain degree of involvement, thus entailing a need to know about that which is communicated.

As a last resort, the involvement of the audience in the journalistic discourse, Muñoz Torres goes on to say, depends on the fact that they can capture the "essential meaning" of the discourse. Given that journalistic discourse represents different types of free human actions, and in view of the fact that the life of man is a constant taking of decisions in search of happiness, then the messages in narrative journalistic discourse "become paradigms of behaviour which act as a reference point for the reader or viewer with regard to what should be done or avoided in any given situation".

Some documentaries deal with the subject of human behaviour because, in principle, the public finds them interesting. This seems to be the case, for example, in documentaries with an anthropological content, which deal with issues concerning human nature and the life of man in society. On the other hand, it can be assumed that other documentaries such as those which deal with nature are less interesting as they do not touch specifically on man. Yet the audience figures for these documentaries in various countries show that nature programmes occupy the top rating positions within this genre. How can this interest be explained, bearing in mind that, in principle, the subjects which are dealt with do not seem to refer directly to central issues of human life, or to phenomena which can be easily applied, by the public, to everyday life? According to David Attenborough (1997), there are various reasons which explain the success of this type of documentary.

> First of all they deal with living beings, like us. Secondly, these programs do not set out to sell anything. Another reason is that they don't tell us anything horrible about ourselves, but what they do tell us is true; it is the real world, and it is something we can identify with. It is always surprising; nobody knows everything about natural history and it is nearly always beautiful. And these are rare qualities in a television programme. Furthermore, they are serious issues; people do not watch things that lack substance. And, finally, they are timeless, and go to the very heart of things.

The first point which Attenborough makes can be considered in the light of the idea discussed earlier (section 1.3), according to which journalistic discourse acts as a reference point for the behaviour of the public, given that, deep down, it deals with the subject of living beings like man.

In general, of the many factors that make facts interesting Carl Warren (1959: 15) selects eight: "timeliness, proximity, prominence, rareness, conflict, suspense, emotion and consequence". According to Warren, underlying these factors is the fact that the public is drawn to the media to save time, make money, gain popularity, make progress, be more comfortable and enjoy their free time. To this list, Professor Enrique de Aguinaga (1987: 262) adds a further five factors: "sex, progress, money, usefulness and entertainment".

Other authors throughout history have highlighted these same factors. Muñoz Torres (1996: 97–113) puts the most significant contributions into six categories: spatial; temporal, personal appeal, and public notoriety; the unusual, strange, or unexpected; that which is conflictive and negative; and finally, formal interest.

3.1.1   The Spatial Factor
Generally speaking, a fact is more interesting the closer it is to the realm of the audience. Muñoz Torres distinguishes between the interest derived from physical proximity and that derived from cultural or mental proximity. With regard to the former, science documentaries usually present facts which are taken from anywhere in the world, which at first sight would therefore not be a factor which generates interest. However, it should be remembered that many of these programmes are set in exotic locations, as has been the case since the start of the genre. This preference for the exotic is directly related to another factor of interest, the unusual, which will be discussed in section 3.1.2.

The interest in certain science documentaries, especially those dealing with nature, has increased significantly in the last few decades, coinciding with the growth of ecological-conservationist movements which have contributed to highlighting issues dealing with global problems, all over the world. The dissemination of the idea that the Earth is in danger seems to have also prompted a raised awareness that the planet, as a whole, is the habitat which man should take care of, for his own interest and so it becomes a place which is mentally near.

Warren (1959:18) states that: "for any human being, the most interesting thing is him or herself, and after oneself those things which are closest to oneself, closer mentally and physically: work, health, money, home and family, friends and partners

(…)". In some science documentaries there is a prevailing aim to bring reality closer to the human experience. Those that deal with animals and plants usually attribute them with human characteristics or attitudes in such a way that life in nature appears to be very similar to human activity; even to life in society.

The work of David Attenborough offers some examples of this aim to draw the subject closer to man. In the series *The Trials of Life* (episode 7, sequence7), which deals with the life of parasites, the narrator brings together both realities by saying "We ourselves can become infected with ticks". A similar example can be found in *The Private Life of Plants* (episode 3, sequence 1). This program, about flowers, starts with a shot of the presenter, Attenborough, sneezing while he explains how he suffers from hay fever produced by pollen. The programme goes on to deal with pollen and its function in the life cycle of plants. In this case, the reference to a common ailment allows the everyday concerns of the public to draw them closer to a reality which, in principle, might seem distant.

As Calvo Hernando (1977: 189) points out, there are times when the identification of two elements takes on the form of metaphor, establishing a bridge that is characteristic of scientific discourse, which unites "two realities, one known by the reader and another unknown, one enlightening the other". This rhetorical figure is valuable in science documentaries as can be seen in the following examples taken from the work of David Attenborough. In one sequence in which all the different parasites that live on a buffalo are mentioned (*The Trials of Life*, episode 7, sequence 20), the narrator concludes by saying that this animal "is a walking zoo". In this way, a familiar reality, "the zoo", substitutes another reality of greater cultural proximity to the viewer, a "colony of parasites". Another similar example can be found at another point in the same program (episode 6, sequence 4). After showing the underground tunnels where some animals live and explaining how they keep the temperature cool, the narrator says, with a sense of humour: "The prairie dog has an air-conditioned home".

Nature documentaries do not usually include scenes that have a direct impact on the everyday life of viewers. Instead it seems that the viewer is looking for entertainment or satisfaction in the search for knowledge. However, some authors believe that nature programmes can play an important educational role within the family, because they show models of behaviour which are natural and, to a degree, transferable to human life. According to this line of reasoning, these types of programmes facilitate the discussion within the family of issues related to human behaviour. Crowther (1994) has suggested that, for some families, nature programmes offer "the opportunity to discuss sexual matters, (…) using the examples of the animals that appear on the screen, thus allowing allusions to be made, so that nobody need feel personally involved".

However, although these documentaries may lead to discussions of this type, it should not be forgotten that animal behaviour is mainly instinctive, whereas human behaviour is mediated by both intelligence and will, in addition to drives and feelings.

3.1.2   The Unusual, Strange or Unexpected

The science documentary frequently uses subjects that try to attract the interest of viewer by presenting the unusual, the strange or the unexpected. This is not surprising given that, in general, the working method in the media seems to follow the criteria Charles Dana (quoted in Warren, 1959: 21) expressed in his now famous phrase: "When a dog bites a man it is not news; but if a man bites a dog, that's news"

Some script writing manuals for television recommend the unusual, or the extreme, as good raw material on which to base news programmes. Science documentaries have also incorporated the interest factor into the narrative. Edwin Slosson, director of the Scientific News Agency *Science Service,* thought that for science to reach the general public it had to adapt itself to the taste of the majority. Slosson reached the following conclusion (in Nelkin, 1990: 92):

> It is not the rule but the exception that attracts the public's attention. The people we aim to reach through the daily press are the same people who, in a fairground, crowd around stalls to see three-headed cows and women with beards, but don't go near the stalls to see the wild animals.

Science is not specifically aimed towards the search for the extraordinary. The results of scientific research are always presented by their authors as provisional, not definitive, at least until the findings have been verified by the scientific community and the body of knowledge is accepted, and is, therefore, no longer extraordinary. Yet, as Tratchman (1981: 10–15) has pointed out, science journalists, in their attempt to entertain the audience, look for the infrequent and even the anomalous.

This search for the unusual puts scientific journalism in permanent danger of falling into sensationalism. Although it seems justifiable for the popularisation discourse to appeal to the audience's taste for the extraordinary, an excessive use of this element could lead to the loss of scientific rigour. However, it does seems that the use of the anomalous, in just measure, can be a useful element in the communication process and the fact that it is used does not necessarily devalue the content of what is being communicated. For Calvo Hernando (1977: 192) there is a certain "sensationalism" that can be understood as "an enriching and positive ingredient in the transmission of science". On the other hand, other authors consider that this recourse should be completely eliminated. Ángel Martín Municio (1986: 6), president of the Spanish Academy of Pure Sciences, criticises the anecdotal approach used by journalists and broadcasters. In his opinion, if science is something serious and profound, scientific articles should not be humorous and superficial.

This tendency within journalism and broadcasting to deal with issues in a superficial way is related, ultimately, to the fact that this type of discourse is generally aimed at satisfying the immediate curiosity of the public, for which reason it is not necessary to maintain the same degree of attention as is needed in science.

And these attitudes on the part of the audience are, in turn, related to the distinction between *studiositas* (studiousness) and *curiositas* (curiosity). According to Pieper (1988: 288–293), these two concepts represent the diametrically opposed poles of cognitive desire and the difference between the two is marked by moderation or the absence of moderation in the perception of the world. In this sense, *curiositas* is the attitude of the person who is content with a superficial knowledge of reality and one which hardly requires any attention, while *studiositas*, requires sustained attention and seeks depth of knowledge. From this perspective it is possible to see in the work of some good journalists and broadcasters a desire to transmit a certain depth of knowledge. This attitude determines the difference between journalism or broadcasting which manages to communicate scientific knowledge, and that which limits itself to a mere compilation of anecdotes.

David Attenborough (1994) believes that the inclusion of examples of strange behaviour does not in any way invalidate the scientific rigor of his programmes. Quite the contrary, in his opinion, one of the things that serves to verify the truth of a scientific proposition is the search for a really strange case and to see how this fits in. Furthermore, he believes that such criticism is unfounded if the programme in question has a clear story line and uses strange cases in order to attract interest:

> If something is not very usual it will be interesting. And I have nothing against something which is interesting. It may become dangerous if an element is introduced only because it is strange without relating it in any way to the central theme being dealt with, or if outstanding things are only featured without ever placing them within the solid theoretical structure which is present.

3.2 Narrative Techniques

Having considered some of the elements of news interest which are particularly important to be able to understand the way in which film makers create documentaries, we shall now turn to narrative techniques, the study of which allows us to see how the subject matter can be brought closer to the sphere of interest of the public. From the range of different narrative techniques that can be identified in the documentaries which have been studied, there are some that are particularly important in the popularisation of science. Among those that stand out are: the simplification of content, anthropomorphic approaches and the introduction of entertaining elements.

3.2.1   The Simplification of Content

Good scientific documentaries stand out because of their ability to simplify the terms that are used to deal with the subject matter. According to Dorothy Nelkin (1990: 17), journalists and broadcasters simplify scientific issues because they believe that it is the only way that the public will be able to understand them. She considers that simplification is now obligatory, as a result of the influence of television and its particular style of giving information, based on short bursts of content and on images, which leave little margin for in-depth explanations.

Generally speaking, scriptwriters and television producers agree that "medium time" is a scarce commodity, and so it is necessary to restrict wherever possible the content of the subject matter. The general criteria of the BBC (in Wyatt, 1983: 4) for the production of documentaries is that the choice of information that is to be presented should always be that which is strictly necessary. Given the fact that in one single programme it is not possible to cover all the different aspects of a subject, it becomes necessary to select that which is the most novel, interesting and important.

On the need to select information for a documentary, David Attenborough (in Langley, 1985: 21) considers the following:

> People don't remember many of the ideas of a television programme, so the number of points that can be made is limited. It is a mistake to try to introduce too many ideas. You have got to make it perfectly clear which is the most important point, or two.

The first means of simplifying the content is the process which is followed when determining the sequence of ideas which will appear in the documentary. Determining the sequence of ideas is the first and most basic form of simplification documentary producers use. In this process, numerous elements, which could contribute to the development or nuance of the programme, are eliminated. However, these elements would have probably made the understanding of the subject more difficult.

It is significant that the content of many documentaries can be expressed in a few lines of written text. The process followed by the scriptwriter consists of reducing the problem to its essence, and from there, establishing a line of development to which the dynamic of the problem-solution approach is applied. According to Flesch (1960: 226), this is a good way of facing any question as it facilitates finding good ways of communicating ideas.

Occasionally, the way in which the contents are selected distorts the final message. A study conducted prior to the First Iberian-American Scientific Journalism Congress shows that the following is common: "marked attention is given to the secondary elements of the scientific information, to the detriment of the main elements, in order to accentuate the impact on the reader" (Calvo Hernando, 1977: 81). This is precisely one of the challenges faced by any journalist or broadcaster: that the elements which are selected, allow the central theme to be explained in such a way that the content is not limited to secondary issues.

a)   The Treatment of Complex Scientific Matters
One of the most controversial means of simplification is that which is used when eliminating complex issues because, these are, for many people, the kernel of science. Scientific knowledge is, in general, complex, because of its breadth and specialization. However, in popularising discourse, this complexity is not made apparent.

There is a certain controversy among scientists as to whether the simplification of scientific matters necessarily means losing essential meaning. The French palaeontologist Yves Coppens (1994: 16–17) states that, although the attitude of the scientific community is changing, some researchers are still reluctant to broadcast their work, because, when trying to simplify scientific discourse, it is necessary to slightly distort reality. For this reason, these scientists refuse to give up a certain type of specialised terminology, for fear of betraying the truth because of a lack of precision. On the other hand, the Nobel prize laureate Richard Feynman (in Martín Pereda, 1995: 16), writes in his introduction to *Quantitative Electrodynamics: The Strange Theory of Light and Matter* that he tried to achieve maximum clarity and simplicity, after many hours of discussion, without distorting reality.

The issues dealt with in a documentary can be more or less intrinsically complex. But, in every case the scriptwriter must carry out a simplification process. This simplification implies, firstly, the translation of scientific language into everyday language, using the criteria previously mentioned.

According to the model put forward by Fernández del Moral (1994: 124–8), the index of intelligibility determines the percentage ratio between the number of specialised terms and the total number of words that appear in a text. This ratio can be used to establish one of the criteria that distinguishes good popularising discourse; given that, in general, good journalists and broadcasters tend to avoid specialised terms such as scientific names that could be difficult for the general public to understand; i.e. they aim for a high index of intelligibility in their work. This is the case, for example, in the David Attenborough documentaries, illustrated in the following text. It is a fragment from *The Private Lives of Plants* (episode 2, sequence 3) where the process of photosynthesis is explained:

> Leaves are the factories in which plants produce their food. They are powered by the sunshine and they use the simplest of raw materials: air, water and a few minerals. (…) Air seeps into the leaves through the pores on their surface. It circulates

within them and reaches tiny granules that contain a green substance: chlorophyll. This is the key facilitator that uses the energy of the sun to convert carbon dioxide and hydrogen to produce carbohydrates, sugars and starches.

Below is a comparison of this fragment with a scientific text that describes the same biological process (see photosynthesis in *Diccionario de la Naturaleza*, Madrid, Espasa-Calpe, 1987):

The biosynthesis of the organic compounds involves their reduction through a supply of electrons. Specifically, and for example, the reduction of atmospheric carbon dioxide (CO_2) to carbohydrates (CH_2O)x, of nitrates (NO_3) from the earth or the atmosphere to the amino group ($-HN_2$) of the amino acids. Thus, the photosynthesis of cellular material (carbohydrates, proteins, lipids, etc.,) requires:

-a source of energy provided by solar energy.
-a donor of electrons, necessary to generate reduction power
(…) Photosynthesis, also called chlorophyllic function, depending on the chlorophyll photosynthesising pigment, can be verified in the center of some organelles, chloroplasts.

When comparing the two passages, it is important to note that Attenborough talks about "solar energy" instead of "electrons" and "small particles" instead of "chloroplasts". In the same fragment three chemical components are mentioned: carbohydrates, sugars, and starches, which are probably familiar to the general public. On the other hand, the text avoids any reference to components such as glucose, lipids, or proteins, which are probably less familiar to the audience.

Comparing the two explanations of photosynthesis above, it can be seen that none of the statements made by Attenborough contradict any of those in the scientific text. Quite the contrary, it seems that the explanation given, although simple, reflects reality. However, it is clear that certain aspects have been left out, some of which are important to fully understand what photosynthesis is. Some of the chemical components which are the result of the process, for example, have been omitted. Yet this example is a good illustration of the way in which good journalists and broadcasters simplify the subject matter and their extraordinary ability to undertake vast, complex topics and transform them into something which is very simple.

The danger of this type of simplification is, precisely, taking it to such an extreme that the viewer mistakenly believes that he has understood the subject. Attenborough (1997) himself explained this as follows:

> One has to be alert to the use of certain forms of oversimplification that lack precision and that give a false sense of understanding. Things can be simplified and translated into everyday language which you think will help people understand a topic. But really they don't understand. For example, in particle physics, I am sure that people think that particles are like ping-pong balls, and we know that they are not; it's just a simple metaphor. And so you have to be aware of how far you can go with simplification.

b) *Suppressing Controversy*

Another means of simplifying the complexity of science, which is used frequently, is to eliminate controversy. Despite the fact that reality can often have different interpretations, journalists and broadcasters usually present one single explanation, as if this were the irrefutable truth. According to Considine (1986: 42), nature documentaries often use a narrative that "pretends to be omniscient, metonymic of the scientific community, harmonious and disinterested".

This means of simplifying reality is also used by journalists and broadcasters of other scientific disciplines. According to Roqueplo (1983: 123–125), the sciences carry out a type of "cultural terrorism", in spite of the fact that scientific knowledge is constantly being revised and questioned, because they are regarded by the public as being indisputable and having irrefutable teachings. For Roqueplo the paradox can be explained in three ways:

a)   The privacy of scientific disciplines, which prevents non-experts from participating in controversies.
b)   The fact that published texts, once naturalised, are loaded with "ontology" ("this can not be any other way").
c)   The mediation of the mass media, immersed in a process which is unilateral – and therefore indisputable, solitary – and therefore uncritical – and contemplative.

In general, in documentaries, narrators put themselves in positions of omniscience from which they offer the uncontroversial and apparently irrefutable truth, where there is not only no room for scientific controversy, but no room for doubt. In this position there have been instances of extreme forms of oversimplification, considering that models of behaviour that are presented can transform grey areas of science into areas which are either black or white.

c)   *Reducing Dimensions*
Another frequently used means of simplification is to reduce the dimensions of the aspects of reality which are shown. Calvo Hernando (1977:186) points out that the transpositions, "the reduction of facts and numbers to a scale that is more accessible to the imagination, is always well accepted by the public". This humanisation of scale is found in many nature documentaries in the form of a reduction of time scale. One of the most brilliant examples of this type of simplification can be seen in the first episode of David Attenborough's series *Life on Earth* (sequence 15), where the history of mankind is reduced to one single year, so that in this hypothetical calendar man would not have appeared on Earth until December 31st.

Another clear reduction of time is the technique of "time-lapse photography" used in documentaries, which show the movements of plants or other natural phenomena, condensing the movements in such a way that processes which last days, months or years are reduced to a few seconds.

On the other hand, the great majority of documentaries clearly reduce the time span of the events they show. In this way, in an hour-long programme, we can see condensed, for example, an expedition led by Cousteau that lasted, in reality several months. This type of time reduction is found, to a greater or lesser degree, in all audiovisual genres which generally refer to time periods which are longer than the programme itself. Occasionally, the passage of time is suggested through visual transitions such as mixings. On the other hand, transitions between shots are carried out by cuts in the editing, which seem to be an attempt to suggest that all the events which comprise the sequence are presented on the same time scale.

In this sense, it is interesting to note that editors of a prestigious institution like the BBC Natural History Unit, aim to create a single sequence of images by using cuts during the editing, with the result that the action seems to be continuous. However, sometimes the sequences can be completed with images from other moments of the action, or even from archive material.

These reductions in time scale produce a visual simplification which does not result in a change in the content of the issues presented, but rather is a means of making the narrative more agile. In fact, this visual simplification technique has been used since the very first documentaries. As Ellis (1989: 21) points out, the way in which the protagonist in *Nanook* (Flaherty's classic) constructs his igloo is shown so simply and clearly that "we ourselves could go out and build one if they gave us enough snow".

3.2.2 Anthropomorphic approaches

One of the techniques which is most often used in nature documentaries is anthropomorphism; that is to say, the attribution of human forms, characteristics and attitudes to beings that, in reality, do not have them.

Some of Disney's classics, like *The Living Desert,* have been criticised for using this technique to an exaggerated degree, as the animals appear to be human parodies, an effect which is achieved by the montage of contrasting actions and music that accentuates the burlesque effect.

Other documentary producers, like Cousteau, also resort to this technique freely. For example, in his series *Submarine Adventure,* there are numerous references like the following: "the otter, free of any complex" (episode 2, sequence 12) and (among the whales), "the king of the harem attacks" (episode 39, sequence 6).

Félix Rodríguez de la Fuente also humanises animals in a similar way to Cousteau. In his programmes, some animals are attributed with what are clearly human characteristics or modes of behaviour. For example: "the masked dormice must have already celebrated their wedding" (El *hombre y la Tierra-Fauna Ibérica,* El Lirón Careto I (sequence 1) and "the shrike, ruthless, ruins the young masked dormouse's first adventure" (sequence 27).

For some authors, a certain degree of anthropomorphism is inevitable in these types of documentaries, because it provides elements with which to write entertaining scripts. This technique seems to sustain itself because of the conviction that the parallelism accentuates the viewer's interest, given that people more readily understand that which refers to other people, which is what they know best. Furthermore, it should not be forgotten that, on occasions, the emotional behaviour of animals offers objectively strong similarities to man, as the strategies used by animals which confront problems are understandable and familiar to us because we ourselves have to face the same situations.

Anthropomorphism is not a technique which is used only in documentaries but has been used widely in literature, both in narrative and dramatic genres. The first literary genre where human traits are attributed to animals is the fable. From Sumerian, Greek, Latin, Mesopotamian and Indian civilizations, fables have been passed on through traditions and languages, taking on different forms, reaching contemporary civilisation and maintaining its particular critical, satirical and popular characteristics.

Although not all fables feature animals, it is precisely the ones that do that, which are the best known today. According to Rodríguez Adrados (1979: I, 17), this is because the idea of the fable that we have today comes from the collections made in the seventeenth century by La Fontaine and his followers, who mainly collected fables that featured animals.

Classical fables focus, precisely, on confrontations between animals which have been attributed with a series of fixed characters which, in general come from similes from Homer and proverbs or sayings from Classical Antiquity. So, for example, the lion is powerful and strong, the fox is astute, the monkey is vain, and the sheep is stupid.

As in literature, the cinema has also used approaches of this type. Gloria Toranzo (1968: 238) points out that the audiovisual media is able to attribute to objects a role which is similar to that of man, as a close up enables this object to "speak". Toranzo also points out that anthropomorphism is a common element in any communicative process, because there is a general tendency in language to attribute human qualities to inert, animate or abstract concepts.

Science has also turned to anthropomorphism, in order to explain how its sees the world. For Gerald Holton (in Preta, 1993: 32) "the strength of many scientific concepts which are extremely useful, rests on the fact that, at least in part, they are mere anthropomorphic projections of the world of human matters".

Even from the times of ancient Rome, the perception of animal behaviour was imbued with anthropomorphic interpretations. Specifically in zoology in the first century BCE, the naturalist Pliny refers to elephants in the following terms:

> Of the animals on Earth, the elephant is the largest and the one whose intelligence is closest to that of man, because it understands the language of its country, obeys orders, has a good memory, likes love and honour, and also possesses a rare quality even among men: self-control and a sense of justice. It

> also adores the stars and worships the sun and moon (in Drickamer and others, 1986: 9).

Throughout history, zoology has frequently held anthropomorphic positions in order to transmit knowledge. According to Drouin (1992: 302–303) a certain degree of anthropomorphism within this scientific discipline is justifiable:

> Anthropomorphism, so frequently discredited, is often inevitable. How else can you describe the flee of a prey without evoking its fear, the strategy of a predator without talking about shrewdness, the search for a partner without saying the word seduction?

On occasions there have also been searches within zoology for ways to explain human behaviour. According to Drouin the transmission of zoological knowledge has traditionally had, in addition to an explicitly educational function, a second implicit function:

> To enlighten man about himself (…) To present human activity as a repetition, somewhat more elaborate, of animal behaviour is a recurrent theme in scientific dissemination. Its aim is usually to give man a lesson in humility.

Both the animalisation of human behaviour and the anthropomorphic description of animal behaviour have been common for many centuries. However, it is from the beginning of the eighteenth century that this identification becomes more frequent among scientists and journalists.

Modern zoology tends to reject anthropomorphism. According to the British zoologist Colin Tudge (1994: 19) "throughout most of this century animal psychology has been dominated by behaviourism, in which anthropomorphism is a mortal sin".

Behaviourist psychology, started by J.B. Watson at the beginning of the twentieth century, considers the objective observation of behaviour as the only way to understand human behaviour, rejecting everything which is subjective (sensations, thoughts, etc.). As Tudge points out, the origin of the behaviourist approach as applied to animal behaviour comes from the seventeenth century, when Descartes affirmed that animals could not think since they lacked a language similar to that of humans. This animal behaviourism was also reinforced by the positivist approach, which defended the idea that science should only study that which can be measured or verified. Given that animal thoughts and feelings could not be measured, they should be ignored.

However, as Tudge rightly points out:

> Many scientists openly talk about animal 'thought'. Everybody, from zookeepers to psychology professors, argue about the 'stress', 'happiness', 'depression', or 'boredom' of animals.

These similarities between animal and human behaviour, suggest that, according to Tudge, anthropomorphism should not be totally discarded because, if it is correctly used, it can be very revealing. These claims by the zoologist are not surprising if we consider, along with the philosopher Jacinto Choza (1988: 25), that man shares with animals the ability to sense, that is to say, they have sensations, perceptions, tendencies and affection. What distinguishes man from other animals is his capacity to carry out intellectual and wilful actions. In other words, for animals, objectives are "philogenetically programmed" in that they know the goal of their actions even if these are predetermined beforehand; it could be said that their lives are ruled by outside forces". In the case of man the aim of his activities, including nutrition and reproduction, are not "philogenetically programmed, instead they are individually set depending on a more complex, individual apprenticeship".

3.2.3   *Entertainment Factors*
It is common for journalists and broadcasters to introduce elements into their work, in order to make the result more engaging.

This resource is used regularly in audiovisual communication. Some manuals on audiovisual script writing recognise the importance of entertaining the audience throughout the programme. For example, Berger (1990: 12), states that in order to achieve this objective, the style of a programme should be more entertaining than that of an essay.

This use of elements which make the communication more interesting is not exclusive to audiovisual discourse, but is also a frequent resource used in literary works. In this field, it is considered that elements such as anecdotes are an ideal tool to maintain the interest of the audience in current affairs items.

The development of the popularisation of science has often been associated with events or spectacles clearly aimed at entertaining or amusing the public. And so, the presentation to society of scientific discoveries was usually through public events. The work of science journalists also considers this need to entertain, to the extent that on occasions, it goes further than capturing the interest of the audience and distorts the text, by eliminating essential information or using it without the necessary scientific rigor. In this context, the study conducted prior to the First Iberian American Conference on Scientific Journalism (in Calvo Hernando 1977: 81) illustrates the frequent error of "almanacism", a tendency to transform information which is educational, scientific, and technological into curiosities, notes and anecdotes, etc. On this point Fernández del Moral (1986: 4) considers that this danger can only be avoided to the degree that the journalist or broadcaster has the conviction that "to spread ideas is not to trivialise but to incorporate new knowledge that requires above all an effort in the models of communication".

The analysis of programmes by good journalists and broadcasters shows that information and entertainment can be interwoven. David Attenborough (1994) believes that the three traditional functions of television should be unified in a programme, given that entertainment should be one of the pillars of any educational activity:

Information, education and entertainment are all the same. They really are. You cannot educate without entertaining, that is the first lesson for a teacher (...) and information is what education is about. Really it is all the same.

3.3 Dramatic Techniques

Since the beginning of the genre, there have been some documentaries that have represented reality using techniques that are characteristic of works of fiction. In the notion of the documentary as proposed by Grierson – the creative treatment of actuality – is found implicitly the use of dramatic techniques. In fact, the programmes produced within the movement he started quite often use reconstructions, which bring the documentary closer to the field of drama.

This use of dramatisation reached one of its high points when the documentary unit of the BBC, directed at first by Paul Rotha, a close follower of Grierson, was established. At the time, in the range of programmes which this unit produced, were those which were called "dramatised documentaries" that dealt with real events, using actors who performed according to a previously written script. An internal BBC document (Wyatt 1983: 3) on these "dramatised documentaries" states that "the more convincing they are as dramas, the fewer objections the audience have and the less importance they give to understanding, omissions, or imaginative padding out". This claim suggests that the public accepts the use of dramatic techniques in programmes dealing with real situations, the deciding factor being their success as drama.

Similarly, science broadcasting on television tends to adopt determined dramatic forms. As Aubrey Singer, director of scientific programmes for the BBC, (in Silverstone, 1986: 140) points out, science television "is subject to the principles of structure and the demands of the dramatic form. Therefore; the decision-making process should give priority to the medium, rather than to scientific pedantry".

Professional journalists also refer to the dramatic component which is found in some reports. An internal document from the

North American television channel NBC (in Berger, 1990: 120) makes the following recommendations:

> Each news report should possess, without sacrificing authenticity and responsibility, the features attributed to fiction or drama. It should have structure and conflict, problem and development, increasing action and decreasing action, a beginning, middle and end. These are not only the essential elements of drama; they are the essential elements of narrative.

With regard to the use of dramatic techniques in audiovisual communication, other authors have discussed this from a theoretical point of view. García Avilés (1990: 610) believes that these techniques give news reports "greater clarity, interest and narrative force" because the viewer is already familiar with fiction programmes and easily understands narrative that is structured in this way.

Documentaries and fiction programmes can even have a similar gestation process. There are those who call for the suppression of the false dichotomy; documentary film versus fiction film, given that both categories share common elements in their discourse. This is better understood if we consider that, as Zunzunegui (1989: 150) suggests, "every fiction film documents its own narrative (through the analogous act of filming) and all documentary films fictionalise a pre-existing reality, by choosing which point of view to take". Furthermore, it should be remembered, along with Bill Nichols (1991: 107), that sometimes the documentary is converted into fiction with a plot, characters, tension, conflict and resolution; from which it can be deduced that documentaries are, in fact, constructions which are used to refer to reality, rather than to reproduce reality itself.

Nichols (1991: 15) reminds us that works of fiction are also usually set in such a way that they are clearly connected to the real world, by the use of costume, furniture, scenery, etc. However, fiction has greater artistic licence in other respects; for example, the audience accepts the fact that historical characters of any nationality speak English. In any case, it is important not to forget, as Nichols points out, that the essential difference between a fiction film and a documentary film is the representation they use, given that "in the heart of the documentary there is not so much a story and its imaginary world, as an *argument*, about a historical world" (1991: 115).

The use of dramatic techniques in news programmes and documentaries has been criticised, because they can create a certain degree of confusion in the viewer. In this regard, García-Noblejas (1990: 54) mentions that in contemporary communicative texts there is an increase in "the ambiguity between what is natural and what is artificial, between the reality of fiction and the fiction of reality". Arruti (1991: 412) adds that the biggest danger that threatens structured information with dramatic criteria is that reality is falsified so that the story becomes interesting. Although Arruti acknowledges the difficulty of representing reality objectively, he believes that programmes of this type jeopardise the objectivity of information.

In a similar vein, Roger Silverstone (1986: 89) criticises the fact that, in the move from the laboratory to the communication media, scientific texts are converted into "fairytales". Elsewhere, Silverstone (1985) carries out a detailed study of the gestation process and the final outcome of a BBC science documentary for the *Horizon* programme. In this study it is clear that the documentary, which was analysed, undertook a search for dramatic elements, such as heroes and villains and a story with a strong emotional charge.

For his part, Lyotard (1984) deals with the relationship between science and narrative, from the standpoint that, in its essence, science, not only does not use stories to legitimise itself, but instead enters into conflict with them as they have, at their heart, fables. However, in the midst of the fragmented culture of the post-modern world, science has needed to resort to stories to legitimise itself; that is to say, to present a series of conditions that allow it to be recognised as science and form part of everyday knowledge.

Silverstone responds to Lyotard's statements by analysing scientific texts and highlighting that these also contain dramatic elements. In principle, science uses *mimesis* (imitation of reality), as a means of construing arguments and appealing to reason. On the other hand, everyday knowledge uses mythical categories to formulate stories that are aimed primarily at our emotions. However, according to Silverstone, on occasions science also uses mythical categories, just as everyday knowledge uses *mimesis*. The scientific communication which was analysed in the study used the problem-solution approach, in the midst of which the author was portrayed as hero (helped by other scientists). The enemies were those scientists whose research results the author challenged and the solution to the problem which was posed constituted the desired aim.

David Attenborough (1987: 12) is openly in favour of using certain dramatic techniques in his documentaries. In his opinion, if the aim of these programmes is to communicate the mysteries and wonders which lie hidden in nature, then the film producer should have the "maximum flexibility in production in order to achieve it (…) and should allow the introduction of fiction into natural history programs". In his work it is in fact possible to identify some dramatic techniques. They are used, above all, in some sequences whose only purpose is to illustrate the narrative. In this sense, it can be said that Attenborough uses a dramatic structure which is less marked than that used by other documentary makers such as, for example, Cousteau and Rodríguez de la Fuente.

Of the dramatic techniques used by these and other authors, particularly important are those which are related to the use of stories, the consideration of characters involved in conflict situations and the search for suspense.

3.3.1 *Story construction*
The idea of the journalist as "story-teller" is widespread. However, when this concept is examined more closely, the idea that all information discourse tells a story does not hold. It seems

appropriate, therefore, to define the concepts of story and narrative. Generally speaking, a story is a set of real or fictional actions or events which took place in the past, with respect to the time of narration. A narrative is the coherent representation, in a sequential form, of a story.

The kind of representation that uses a narrative is appropriate for discourse in which the aim is not to present all the details of reality with "exhaustive mechanics", as is the case with history or science, but in the form of "quick and essential totality". As García-Noblejas (1982: 203) points out, this quick and essential totality is not exclusive to fiction:

> (…) it is not univocally associated with fiction, to the degree that it presupposes the presence of (…) maxims or affirmations which are veritable, orientated towards a necessary knowledge of things, prior to judgement on these.

The ability of man to tell and understand stories was understood long before documentary makers came along. Since time immemorial, people have considered the ability to tell stories, and numerous authors have written about this. Alastair McIntyre (1987: 266) states that man "as much in his actions and customs, as in his fiction, is essentially an animal that tells stories". Similarly, Forster (1983: 332) says that the act of telling stories "goes back to the Neolithic period, perhaps even the Palaeolithic. Neanderthal man listened to stories, as far as we can tell according to the shape of his skull".

With the aim of understanding the construction of stories in science documentaries, it is worthwhile remembering, beforehand, some of the approaches carried out in this regard by other documentary makers. It is also appropriate to summarise the thoughts of some of the many authors who have written about this subject, in particular Aristotle, originator of the poetic and dramatic tradition which continues to today.

Some kind of narrative can also be found in numerous news items. In English news items are called *stories* and often adopt the structure of a short narrative, in which a protagonist carries out a series of actions. As López Pan (1997: 50–51) points out, the term *story* does not exactly coincide with the term "narrative", as it often refers simply to the theme or matter being dealt with. However, it is not uncommon for English and American journalists to write their items as a *story,* while in other areas of journalism (newspapers and television) this structure is not predominantly found.

Within the documentary genre, even from its inception, many of the prominent documentary producers have structured the content of their work so as to tell a story. Flaherty organizes his documentaries following the actions of specific characters, such as the hunter *Nanook* or the main character, the young adolescent, in *Moana*. British documentary producers also frequently use specific stories to structure their work, even though they are not always centred on people.

However, there are times when the documentary is not structured around a story, in the above sense of the word, but instead limits itself to a thematic organisation of the subject. When this structure is used, it is common practice to start with an introduction to the subject, to continue with a development of the details and to end with some type of conclusion. The aim, therefore, is to give a representation of past events, given that the subjects chosen are also often abstract ideas, for example, tendencies, which are not strictly speaking concrete facts. Furthermore, in these cases the information is not structured following the development of events, but instead follows the criterion of thematic proximity between the different subjects considered, i.e. in these cases, the documentary does not tell a story.

Within the category of documentaries structured in the form of a story, it is important to distinguish, along with Feldman (1990: 56–7), between those that follow a linear narrative of events and those that tell a story in dramatic terms. In the linear structure, which is frequently found in the tradition of eastern countries, events are described linearly, like that of a journey or path, during, or on which, different events take place. In the dramatic story, which stems from the Greek tragedy, the narrative is structured around the start, development and closure of a conflict (beginning, middle and end).

The use of a linear dramatic narrative aims, in short, to highlight the difference between a story on the one hand, and a straightforward chronological narrative or succession of events, on the other. According to Claude Bremond (1966: 62), to produce a story there should be a "succession of human interest events, within the unity of the same action". In the event that the action is not unified, viewers find themselves before a broadcast comprising successive events.

In the tradition of Western civilization, the first reference to the concept of unity of action appears in Aristotle's *Poetics* (1451, 30–35):

> The truth is that, just as in the other imitative arts one imitation is always of one thing, so in poetry the story, as an imitation, must represent one action, a complete whole (…).

According to this Aristotelian tradition, still valid today, action, which should comprise of more than one event, should be complete and have a certain "magnitude". For the action to be complete it should have a beginning, middle and an end. For an action to have magnitude it should not be so big that it loses unity or so small that the vision is confusing. Finally, from the point of view of the structure of the action, magnitude implies that the "transition from adversity to happiness or from happiness to adversity" should take place and be noted without difficulty.

In the context of science documentaries it is also common to structure the content around stories, whether they be dramatic or linear. According to the British writer and director Hugh Falkus (1976: 169), the entire production procedure of nature programmes should always begin with a story. The presence of a story serves as a narrative thread and fulfils the function of guiding viewers and helping them to understand what is being told. As Boswall (1993) points out, the viewer "should know, at any given moment, where he is, if this is not the case it should be because of choice, not error". In agreement with Boswall, producing a nature documentary by means of story has as its aim the transformation of a series of scientific facts into an artistic broadcast imbued with unity and variety. In these types of documentaries, Boswall goes on to say, unity is more difficult to achieve than variety, given that science pursues facts and is constantly branching out its reasoning. Therefore, it is especially important that a documentary follows a story, through which it can construct a unified whole.

Both linear stories and stories based on drama have the same aim, which is to interest viewers in what is being told, so that they want to continue watching the programme, to see what happens next. This is more easily achieved using drama, as it is easier for the viewer to feel involved in the story given that it deals with a unified, human-interest action. This approach also allows for the emotional involvement of the viewer as the programme can play on feelings. Furthermore, conflict is usually presented in such a way that its resolution presents viewers with doubts, thus creating moments of suspense, which encourage more attentive viewing of the development of the programme.

Nature documentaries, generally speaking, have in their background, stories based on fables that are used as *leitmotivs*. As Barbara Crowther (1994) points out, the three most characteristic stories are "the life cycle", "the search narrative" and "the triumph of science over nature".

"The life cycle" fable does not follow, as would be expected, the process from birth to death, but instead, usually follows the process from birth to reproduction. The second type of fable which underlies these programmes is that of the naturalist as hero, a man on an expedition in search of something. This story, also found in many children's stories, has been adopted by nature documentaries in the form of a naturalist or researcher on a scientific journey or expedition. Good examples of the use of this type of fable are the programmes made by Cousteau that generally follow a journey made by the naturalist and his team. In his programmes, the journey the scientists take becomes the backbone of each programme, and onto this are added sequences of animal life. In this way, each programme tells a clear story with a few characters (Cousteau and his team), with a common aim (the scientific mission), who overcome difficulties (the forces of nature), to finally reach their goal.

The three types of fables which have been highlighted can be found in many programmes made by documentary producers. Rodríguez de la Fuente usually resorts to the fable of the naturalist as hero and also to the triumph of science over the mysteries of nature. For example, in the previously mentioned episode of *Fauna Ibérica* on the masked dormouse (I sequence 2) this animal is portrayed as a character "that has the appearance and perhaps all the subtlety of a little elf". The narrative envelops this small rodent with a mysterious environment, which is revealed, in part, when the camera focuses on the tree trunk where the animal is hiding.

These fables tend to reinforce the dramatic feeling of a programme and therefore bring the content closer to viewers' everyday means of acquiring knowledge. However, as Crowther (1994) suggests, they are stereotyped formulas that close the door to other narrative modes which could perhaps better serve the aim of disseminating "hypothetical and interpretative aspects of science and allow for a greater freedom in the endings, more varied perspectives, and different voices".

David Attenborough (in Langley, 1985: 21) is in favour of organising the content of his programmes by following a story which acts as a "narrative thread". This thread can be found as much within sequences as in an episode as a whole and throughout a complete series. When there is a strong narrative thread in a program it is considered by the scriptwriter as a treasured "gift from heaven", because it is "not enough to have an easy or logical succession of images." Attenborough (1997) adds that, in this way, it is possible to keep the viewer's interest in what is being said.

> The best programs are like stories; they all have a narrative in which you want to know what is going to happen next. This is just as valid for a detective novel as it is for a science programme, given that science is interesting because it throws out a question and the viewer wants to know the sequence of events that will finally lead to the answer to the question, which will, in turn, lead to another question.

In his opinion, the search for the story should not be taken "to the extreme of distorting the truth of what is being told, but if the elements of a story are there, then they should be used" (1977).

As has been shown, one of the main concerns of broadcasters and journalists is finding "good stories" as raw material for their work. This notion, frequently imprecise, often leads to the choice of material that lends itself to a story-telling format, in terms which are close to fiction.

However, one should not lose sight of the fact that the story is not the only tool available to documentary producers with which to keep the viewers' interest. In some cases the strength of the subject is such that a simple guiding thread can achieve this aim. This is the case of the film *Winged Migration* (*Le peuple migrateur*, 2001), by the French director Jacques Perrin. In this case, the visual strength of the film is enough to keep the viewer's interest, although no conventional story is told.

Furthermore, it is easy for the search for stories with a strong narrative potential to distort reality, by applying certain narrative categories. This danger is well pointed out by Arruti (1991: 412) for whom the biggest risk facing information structured according to this model is that reality is distorted to make the final story more appealing.

In some cases, the report or documentary is narrated using terms that are so similar to the discourse used in fiction that it can lose credibility as a broadcast dealing directly with the real world. Experience suggests that there is a point of proximity to fiction, from which the viewer no longer believes that what is being told is true.

3.3.2 Considering Real Beings as Characters

From the beginning of this genre, some documentary producers based their work on characters. Robert Flaherty was one of the first to structure his films following the actions of a central character. The first version of *Nanook* was structured following a thematic order, in the style of the documentaries of that period. When the first version was finished a fire destroyed all the footage. When, years later, Flaherty managed to again make his film about Eskimos, he decided to do so by following one single person: the hunter Nanook. His later work also used a similar format and after him many other documentary producers "converted" real people into characters, around whose actions the story, which constituted the documentary, would develop.

This approach becomes almost inevitable, given that when a documentary aims to tell a story it has to do so through one or more characters. For this reason, it is no surprise that some authors, like Miller (1980: 119), recommend personalizing stories, as a human face helps the viewer identify with the subject matter.

In the field of the nature documentary, there is a well-known technique of making animals and plants into characters. For example, in one of his programmes, (*The Masked Dormouse* I, sequence 6) Rodríguez de la Fuente explicitly refers to the dormouse as "the protagonist of our story" and refers to the animal as "an elf, that is going to begin one of the most wonderful adventures of his life". In the same programme one of the enemies of the masked dormouse is presented as a "master vixen", thus giving it a clear portrayal as a literary character.

The characterizations used by Cousteau are less explicit. However, the animals which appear in his documentaries are also presented, to a certain degree, as characters which take part in a story. Cousteau refers, for example, to penguins as being faithful to their spouses during the mating season (*Submarine Adventure,* "The Flight of the Penguins", sequence 7). In this way, it is suggested that these animals are capable of taking moral decisions, eclipsing the fact that they act according to instinct.

It is in these types of characterizations that some authors have seen ethical connotations, for which reason they are linked to the moral rating of these actions. Quintero Meza (1991: 394–5) refers to this issue as follows:

> Information as a narrative transmits an ethical standpoint, for which reason it situates the protagonist within a world with a sense of finality, where actions are related to the idea of good or evil, in accordance to the final goal which is proposed in each case.

In the same vein, Roger Silverstone (1985: 170) criticizes the fact that certain television programmes carry out a search for heroes and villains. According to Silverstone, documentaries tend to look for characters that can be included in one of these two categories, so as to adapt the programme to what viewers are used to.

David Attenborough (1994) is in favour of using this technique because, for him, a good script is "a good story, in which you worry about who is in it and what is going to happen". From his point of view it is totally justified to consider animals as characters who take part in a story:

> Not only do I justify thinking of them as characters, they are characters. I mean, these are animals I can identify. To give an example, in a sequence with a whale and a sea lion, I know her, that she is female, that she has been coming here for the last 10 years, that she had a son last year, who is right by her side, and that she always behaves in a certain way. That is what happens, there's no exaggeration, I don't make it up. How else could I tell this story? Of course they're characters.

This approach becomes evident in various sequences in which some animals and plants take on roles as characters, whose desires trigger the actions shown. In general, characters appear to be cast as beings equipped with a tremendous ability to solve the problems or conflicts that nature presents to them. And, as has been mentioned when discussing the anthropomorphic approach, these abilities usually produce actions which seem to be carried out freely, instead of being the result of a biological necessity.

3.3.3   Elements of Conflict and Suspense

As discussed earlier (section 3.3.1), some documentaries use a dramatic structure in which one or more characters comes face to face with conflict. This approach is very common, not only in science programmes but also in other documentaries and news reports.

The study carried out between 1984 and 1986 by McCartney (1987: 163) on the content of daily newspapers, magazines, and television news broadcasts, shows that situations involving conflict can be found, usually, in the main news stories and reports published by the media. This study shows that in the media there are, at least, eighteen different types of conflict that are repeated in the news items analysed, and concludes that reports are written around conflict because that is what creates interest.

Many television news broadcasts also tend to focus on situations of conflict. In a study on the reports of the programme "20/20", broadcast on the North American channel ABC, Idrovo (1991: 619) points out that these present a structure in which conflict is presented in the format of man versus society or the individual versus the institution. In documentaries it is also common to aim to keep viewer interest by positioning a series of obstacles or conflict situations in the path of characters, as they move towards their goals. As Feldman (1990: 83) points out "without obstacles, there is no conflict and without conflict there is no interest".

In his typology of documentaries, Nichols (1991: 19) differentiates between four modes of representation: expository, observational, interactive, and reflexive. The expository mode is that which is used in traditional documentaries (Flaherty, Grierson, etc.), in which an omnipresent voice completes the information presented through the images. The mode based on observation, as used in *direct cinema* (Leacock, Pennebaker, etc.), is that which aims to record reality, trying to make the presence of the camera interfere as little as possible, if at all, on the subject. The third mode, termed interactive, was used by documentary producers in *cinema verité* and aims to find people's reactions in front of a camera, thus highlighting, at the same time, the role of the film producer. Finally, in the reflexive mode, as can be seen in work like *Man with a Camera*, by Vertov, the role of the film maker forms part of the documentary. Expository documentaries usually present a problem that is later analysed and finally solved. On the other hand, documentaries based on observation present structures which are closer to those of a conflict that has to be resolved. However, according to Nichols, the dynamics of problem-solution is always present. The point of view presented by Nichols suggests that, independently of the narrative mode used, the presence of conflict is the very essence of many documentaries.

In the case of nature documentaries, conflict always appears to be related to the struggle of living things to survive. These conflicts are of three types: an individual facing a hostile environment, an individual against a predator, and finally, an individual face to face with another from the same species, in order to defend territory or compete for females.

Given that these three types of conflict are present in nature itself, the role of the documentary producer is simply to record them, in such a way that the representation reinforces his or her admiration for the reality of nature.

A clear example of the importance of presenting a strong conflict can be found in the documentary *March of the Penguins* (*La marche de l'empereur*, 2005) by Luc Jacquet and Yves Darondeau. This film follows the annual journey of the penguins to their traditional breeding ground in Antarctica. The conflict of surviving under extreme condition is one of the fundamental elements that keeps the viewer's interest.

The aim is not, therefore, to represent conflict through the action of the narrating subject, as occurs, for example in the works of Cousteau. In the latter, conflict appears frequently in the relationship between the scientific team and nature or, in general, between man and the natural world.

When an audiovisual narrative is set up around one or more characters that try to reach certain goals, the possibility arises of using dramatic techniques, similar to those used in the construction of fictional narrative. One of the most important is suspense.

As Eugene Vale (1992:124) states, suspense is the uncertainty produced in the viewer in terms of the character's capacity to reach, or not, his objective. In order to achieve this, it is necessary that the viewer clearly understand the aim of the character and the obstacles which prevent the aim from being fulfilled.

According to Alfred Hitchcock, (in Truffaut, 1974: 59–60), suspense is the most powerful means available to audiovisual narrative to keep the viewer's attention. For this film director, considered to be the master of this technique, suspense is not the same as fear, nor is it comparable to mystery. In a detective film, for example, the mystery as to who the murderer is cannot be considered to be true suspense, as it is more "a curiosity devoid of emotion, and emotion is a crucial ingredient in suspense".

For Attenborough (1997) suspense is an important element, which he specifically looks for when he is researching subjects, and which he bears in mind when writing the script. From his point of view, this importance is logical, because suspense is the ideal tool with which to keep the viewer interested in what is being narrated.

The use of situations of extreme danger has been highlighted as one of the reasons for the success of nature documentaries, as they show extreme situations fights which are a matter of life or death. For this reason, they may have a certain cathartic effect, as they represent actions that would otherwise be excessively harsh in man.

A superb example and an excellent sequence of the use of this technique in a documentary film can be found in BBC's *Leopard. The Agent of Darkness. A Wildlife Special* (1999). Using infrared lenses, the film shows a leopard hunting at night. The sequence, which relies mainly on the image itself, follows the difficulties the animal has hunting, creating in the viewer the feelings of doubt and emotional involvement.

Chapter 4   Rhetorical Techniques

Having analysed some of the narrative and dramatic techniques that can be used to make effective documentaries, we shall now consider this type of programme from a rhetorical point of view. This will give a new perspective that will help us understand, more clearly, how the communication of scientific knowledge to the general public is carried out. Rhetorical analysis is extremely useful as its aim is to help construct a narrative discourse aimed at the general public which is effective. In the words of Reyes (1961: 375) "Science demonstrates and directs itself to those spirits primed for knowledge and education. Rhetoric persuades and directs itself to all men".

In fact, rhetorical analysis can prove to be a clarifying element in a study like this one, which aims to provide an in-depth analysis of the keys to effective communication, given that one of the basic premises developed by rhetoricians is to extract from language all its effective persuasiveness. Those elements of rhetoric whose sole aim is to achieve beauty in discourse will not, therefore, be considered in this study.

The persuasive approach was considered to be the most important at the origin of the art of rhetoric, as understood in Classical Greece. However, over the centuries, rhetoric began to lose its function as the art of finding ways to persuade through verisimilitude in arguments, which were more or less subjective and instead became a set of rules that advocated elegant speech, which could be, on occasions, hollow, pompous and full of sophistry. In the second half of the 20th century, a number of European and North American publications advocated a "new rhetoric", emphasizing its practical nature and using as a basis sciences such as psychology, information science and sociology. In line with this trend, the work of Perelman and Olbrechts-Tyteca, *La Nouvelle Rhétorique. Traité de l'Argumentation*, is of particular interest. This work provides a wide panorama of the forms of persuasion, based, in great part, on Aristotelian and Renaissance doctrine. Following this reinstatement within the context of practical philosophy, driven decisively by Perelman, rhetoric became a tool used by sociology, psychology and communication sciences. The terms used were among others: literary rhetoric, scientific rhetoric, publicity rhetoric and image rhetoric. According to Silverstone (1986: 90), today, television is perhaps the rhetorical medium par excellence, as it uses language which is essentially figurative (images are metaphors, synecdoches or metonyms of the real world) and makes use of ephemeral messages directed at a wide audience.

The aim of the following sections is, therefore, to analyse the communicative mechanisms through which journalists and broadcasters try to rationally persuade the viewer of the veracity and interest of the issues which are presented. These mechanisms or techniques aim, above all, to establish a solid and effective contact between the author and the public. As Perelman (1989: 51) points out, the fact that someone attempts to rationally convince others, presupposes a certain degree of modesty on the part of the formulating subject, as they are aware that there is no absolute, unquestionable truth. Rhetoric is unnecessary when the truth is self-evident but it is meaningful when working in the field of what is credible, plausible and probable. Or, in Aristotle's words, (Rhetoric I 1355b), rhetoric is meaningful given that "what is persuasive is so for someone immediately by itself or because it seems logically valid".

In order to convince, it is necessary for the speaker to connect with the audience so that between them a community of interests, an intellectual community, is established. When someone addresses a specialist audience (for example, when giving a scientific presentation), the speaker takes it for granted that this connection is already there. In which case, it is enough to get straight to the point for the audience to become interested in what is being said. However, in the majority of cases, the public does not have this predisposition and it is necessary to win over their attention. In the case of science popularisation, this community of interests does not exist *a priori*, so the populariser must do everything possible to establish one. It is for this reason that rhetorical techniques stand out, as a useful tool to analyse the mechanisms by which popularisation connects with the public.

Once this community of interests has been established, it is possible to set up a series of relationships between the speaker and the listener. In the words of Lausberg (1966: 59),

> The listener can be considered by the speaker in his speech and can be addressed in it: 1) as a referee of a decision with the aim, on the part of the speaker, of activating the role of the listener 2) only as spectator that passively enjoys the result (intended or not by the speaker) of the aesthetic interest of the listener in the matter (*res*) and the literary formulation (*verba*) of the discourse.

Aristotle distinguishes two cases of the listener as referee, according to the time in which the subject is set. If it is set in the past, the speaker considers the listener to be a judge; on the other hand, if the subject is set in the future, the listener is in the position of a member of an assembly, which has to take political decisions. It is from this distinction that the three classical rhetorical genres arise: the judicial (*genus iudiciale*), the deliberative (*genus delberativum*) and the demonstrative or epideictic (*genus demostrativum*).

The judicial genre aims to address forensic needs, whether they be accusatory or for the defence. In this case the speaker addresses the person who must judge the evidence which is presented, aiming to establish whether evidence that appears to be just or unjust (*iustum-iniustum*). In the deliberative genre there are speeches such as those where the speaker addresses a public assembly, in order to advise on or warn against future action. To do this, the speaker mainly uses the useful-useless alternative (*utile-inutile*). The epideictic genre (in which narratives such as the documentaries on which this study is based would be included), focuses on matters that are certain and completed, and where no judgement is demanded of the public. In this case, the speaker aims to convince the public of the qualities or defects of the subjects of the discourse, whether they are people, animals or objects.

4.1 Science Documentaries as Epideictic Discourse

Given that the types of documentaries in this study belong to the epideictic genre, it would be appropriate to present some of the characteristics of the discourse of this rhetorical genre, with the aim of drawing conclusions, which can then be applied to these types of programs.

Epideictic discourse does not aim to prompt the listener to make a judgement or take a decision, but rather it aims to please and delight the audience. A typical example is praise for a person or something that needs to be celebrated. In the words of Aristotle (Rhetoric I, 1366 a), epideictic discourse has as its objective "virtue and vice, that which is noble and that which is base", virtue being "the power to create and preserve things and the ability to produce much and great good (...)" The speaker can use aspects of virtue in the search for arguments to extol. These aspects are: justice, courage, moderation, open-mindedness, magnanimity, magnificence and prudence. With these tools, speakers produce speeches with which they aim to convince the public, by praising or condemning that which is the subject of the speech. But rather than pay attention to the subject which is praised or condemned, the public pays attention to the speech itself, which is seen as an occasion to practice the art of oratory. This search for art for art's sake, aims, in effect, to win over the public to the cause, by first gaining admiration for the speech itself.

Subjects which can most easily be adapted to this type of discourse are highly aesthetic objects or topics, because the speaker can describe and praise their beauty. It is no surprise, therefore, that epideictic speech has often been considered as being closer to literature than to rhetoric. In fact, Roman rhetoricians left the study of this genre to grammarians, keeping for themselves the two other genres. However, Perelman (1979: 96–97), rightly points out that epideictic speech constitutes an essential part of the art of persuasion, and attributes the lack of consideration history has given this genre to an erroneous vision of the effects of rhetoric. Perelman reminds us that Demosthenes (considered to be one of the models of classical eloquence), did not limit himself to the search for intellectual support from his fellow citizens, but aimed that they should put into practice the decisions they had taken. From this perspective, therefore, epideictic speech is extremely important as a means of persuasion.

This same idea was formulated differently by Todorov (1977: 59), who states that rhetoric understands language not so much as a form, but as something directed towards action. And, in this sense, rhetoric focuses on the functions of speech, not on its structure. Todorov would later go on to affirm that the emergence of modern aesthetics coincides with the end of rhetoric, given that they both have so much in common their coexistence is not possible.

However, not all discourse harbours the aim to prompt the public into action. For example, the majority of television news programmes do not assume that viewers will act, but rather that they will simply accept the ideas which are presented. The aim of these programmes is, in principle, to faithfully reflect reality. This imitation is achieved by frequently extolling those values which are generally accepted by the audience, aiming to increase the general support for them. On television today there are a number of values or ideals that are a constant feature in the background of many programmes: for example democracy, freedom, tolerance and saving the environment.

This allusion to commonly held values is one of the characteristics of epideictic speech, in which the qualified speaker usually expresses a series of shared ideals or values with the audience, with the aim of reinforcing the audience's support of these. For this reason, as pointed out by Perelman (1989: 103), when in a speech of this type someone takes advantage of the circumstances to refer to values that are not accepted by all, the audience has the sensation of being used. For example, a funeral is an occasion to reinforce certain values or ideals but not to introduce partisan arguments.

Similarly, in educational discourse, the speaker should make reference to universal truths or, at least, to those values that do not introduce controversy into the community which chose the speaker. And, on the contrary, the person who delivers an epideictic speech tends to allude with ease to a universal order and transforms into eternal values those uncontroversial themes that are being dealt with. For this reason it can be said, in agreement with Perelman (1989: 100), that it is in the demonstration that the speaker becomes educator.

Science documentaries implicitly contain some of the values which have been generally accepted in the last few decades, from which the following stand out, for example, the growing importance of science in the modern world and the need to preserve nature against the aggression of human activity.

It can therefore be said that the discourse of science documentaries can generally be situated within the epideictic genre of rhetoric, because these programmes generally refer to values that are not controversial and which are universally accepted. It is precisely these characteristics which have been recognised as one of the keys to the success of scientific documentaries.

4.2   Types of Rhetorical Arguments Used

Having established the epideictic nature of science documentaries, this is now a good moment to pause to consider the types of rhetorical arguments which are used to achieve the aim of transmitting certain aspects of scientific knowledge. The study of the types of arguments used illustrates, once again, the distance which separates scientific discourse and the discourse of popularisation.

Science uses demonstration, above all, as a means of transmitting information. However, it is common for the audience not to understand demonstrations. As Perelman (1979: 10) points out, a demonstration is a formal reasoning process; it is a calculation made using formally established rules, which do not allow for intuition and only take into account that which is detected by the senses. In order to carry out a demonstration, it is necessary to be able to distinguish the signs given by reality, and to execute the operations which are established by the rules accepted by the community.

The public is, frequently, unable to follow a formal scientific demonstration. However, it is necessary to give some type of demonstration as "we give credence, above all, when we understand that something has been demonstrated". This is precisely the area in which rhetorical arguments can be found; a type of reasoning appropriate for popularisation which is based on the opinion of the speaker who hopes that the audience follows the line of reasoning, or, where possible, makes it their own. This distinction is that which separates conviction from simple persuasion. As highlighted by García-Noblejas (1990: 67), persuasion is rhetoric that attempts to motivate listeners of a speech to carry out a specific action. On the contrary, conviction also focuses on the implementation of an action but "firstly, influencing, directly, the attitudes and value systems by modifying or reinforcing them so that from there listeners act in one way or another". Understood in this manner, conviction is more rational, reaches more people and respects more their personal freedom.

Silverstone (1986: 86) suggests that television not only positions itself as mediator between author and audience but also between different types of discourse. This mediation, which is found at the heart of any type of scientific popularisation, is carried out through schemes of argumentation which connect one reality with the daily experience of the audience, using discourse based on myths and stories that are emotionally appealing. These types of narrative schemes which, as has been mentioned previously, can be found in science documentaries, constitute the basis on which argumentation works.

Aristotle (*Rhetoric* I, 1355) differentiates between two types of proof: those pertinent to art and those that are not. The former can be readily used according to the norms of rhetoric, whereas the latter do not depend on the speaker because they already exist:

> I call artless that which is not achieved by us, that which previously exists, like witness accounts, tormented confessions, documents and the like; objects of art are those that through a method and our effort can be available to serve a purpose and be invented if necessary.

Artistic proofs can be of three types: signs, arguments, and examples. Signs are perceptible signals that accompany a fact; arguments are deductive proofs based on facts. Examples are a system of inductive features where what matters is the commemoration of that which is understood, in order to persuade with regard to useful things or events.

By using this distinction, it is possible to highlight the fact that many science documentaries are mainly based on examples. These may be historical, that is to say, taken from reality, or they may be taken from poetry (*fabula*), or comedy (*exemplum verisimile*). The examples used by popularisers are usually historical, which reinforces the credibility of the discourse.

It is possible to consider the examples which appear in these documentaries (for instance, sequences of animal life that comprise a nature programme) as not true examples as such, but rather as non-artistic proofs, which in certain respects, they pre-exist the speech and have a function which is similar to that of witnesses or documents in a forensic report. However, although the images and sounds are taken from reality, they are not used as proofs, valid in themselves, as they are as elements of the discourse which acquire significance only when seen in relation to the other elements.

In addition to examples, these programmes also usually contain arguments. Arguments are deductive and rational proofs based on facts, which are constructed by looking for the proof of the truth of that which is being discussed rather than just its similarity to other elements. As Lausberg (1966: 371) points out, the most perfect form of argument is the syllogism, or reasoning of the following type: "Only virtue is good/ and it is precisely good because of what evil can do/nobody can make ill use of virtue/so virtue is good". By eliminating some of the intermediate elements of this syllogism an enthymeme can be obtained: "Virtue is good: so nobody can make ill use of it".

Some authors consider the enthymeme (abbreviated syllogism) as an imperfect syllogism, given that it does not contain all the elements of the original. Others appreciate the advantages of brevity and credibility which are transmitted to the audience, in comparison to the philosophical syllogism, which, in certain contexts of public speaking, has pedantic connotations. On the other hand, Aristotle (Rhetoric I, 1355a) considered the enthymeme or "rhetorical demonstration" to be "the strongest of arguments". According to Aristotle, all enthymemes should refer to a general consideration and should discuss actions. For example: "Among men there is no one who is free, because he is either a slave to riches or to chance". A speaker should use enthymemes as well as examples, because reasoning through examples is not necessarily less persuasive, "even if those that are more applauded are based on enthymemes". However, Aristotle does concede that some speakers are better at giving examples while others are better at using enthymemes. Later, Aristotle (Rhetoric II, 1395b) specifies that when facing a crowd the ignorant are more persuasive than the educated, since the latter talk about the abstract and the universal, while the former "take from what they know and what is close to the listeners". Reyes (1961: 379) develops this question further stating:

> The average man understands the average man better, responds to the same stimuli, starts with the immediate needs of problems, without worrying about theoretical antecedents, proceeds by jumping over difficult points, is "effectivist" in his reduction of the enthymeme to the maxim, uses reasons and images which do no require lengthy preparation, suppresses stages and runs at the same pace as his listeners.

In the light of such considerations, it is no surprise to find that examples and enthymemes are the two types of proofs most often found in science popularisation. It is also understandable that documentaries, because they are aimed at the general public, use, in addition to examples, some enthymemes, by means of which they can persuade more easily.

In audiovisual discourse there is a tendency to prefer the concrete to the abstract and universal. This fact is the result of the imposition of the medium itself, given that is uses images which are always concrete. However, this justification seems insufficient if one takes into account the fact that audiovisual media have an enormous capacity to communicate ideas, sensations, and emotions that go well beyond the images that are used. The audience knows from experience that certain sequences of images are capable of transmitting abstract ideas, from the sum of the individual images. In television, the overwhelming use of the concrete, as opposed to the abstract, seems to be more related to the fact that its messages are addressed mainly to a wide audience, which, as indicated by Aristotle, are more effective when the arguments are based on the concrete.

But, if the messages aimed at the general public have to preferably resort to the concrete, then popularizing discourse faces the challenge of communicating universal scientific propositions by reducing them to concrete terms. And, in such cases, it could be argued that popularisation is not really transmitting scientific knowledge, as such, but something different. However, as will be seen later, the use of examples within an appropriate structure of argumentation also permits the dissemination of general propositions, even if they are supported by concrete examples.

As discussed previously, many science documentaries are based, fundamentally, on examples, or concrete images. However, the concrete is usually accompanied by propositions, culturally implicit or explicit in the audiovisual expression, that draw universal conclusions from the specific facts shown. In this way, it seems possible to make the demands of being concrete, so typical of audiovisual discourse, compatible with the need to formulate general conclusions as required by science.

The following sections are dedicated to the analysis of the way in which examples and enthymemes are used as the backbone of the argumentative structure of some science documentaries. But, before undertaking this analysis, it is advisable to first make a brief mention of the production process used by these programmes.

4.3 The Production Process (inventio, dispositio and elocutio)

Classical rhetoric distinguishes five phases in the production of a speech (*partes artis*): 1) The search for ideas on the theme to be dealt with (*inventio*). 2) The adequate structuring of these ideas (*dispsitio*). 3) The elocutionary formulation (*elocutio*). 4) The memorisation of the speech (*memoria*). 5) The preparation of its presentation to the public (*actio*).

A detailed study of the way in which each of these phases can be carried out can be found in the thorough compendium by Lausberg (1966: 255–1091). In the present study, only a few of the issues that are particularly relevant will be discussed, with the aim of interpreting the popularisation mechanisms of these documentaries.

The search for ideas, like the other phases in the production of a speech, should have, as its main criterion, the effectiveness of persuasion. In this first phase, the speaker looks for ideas and arguments that imbue the speech with effectiveness, utilising the so-called places (*loci*). These consist of a catalogue of points that serve as a guide to uncover the different facets of an issue. The ideas which are found, either through these research formulae or thanks to the natural talent of the author, should be adjusted to the degree of development of the line of thought as a whole in the speech.

As described in section 3.3.1, documentaries usually decide upon a "line of thought" or "sequence of ideas", with which to start the gestation process of the script. In this way, the possible content of a documentary is drastically reduced. All the information that does not adhere to the adopted line is left out of the programme, even if it is important or significant. It is not, therefore, simply a question of elimination of the information which is less important, but also of eliminating that which does not belong to the established narrative thread. That is to say, as indicated in rhetorical doctrine, the elimination of those ideas which are not in keeping with the adequate degree of development.

This type of simplification may mean abandoning the intention of global understanding that fuels science. In some cases, popularisation discourse does not aim to give essential information on the chosen subject, but rather settles for that which is to be transmitted to be clear and attractive to the viewer. Therefore, one of the greatest challenges for the populariser is not only to make the information which is presented easily understandable, but also to give the audience access to the fundamental questions of the subject in question. If not, it is easy for the programme to become just a series of anecdotes, however perfectly interwoven and interesting they may be.

Once the ideas have been found, the speaker should organise them effectively in order to convince the public. At that point, the principles which govern the presentation come into play: natural order (*ordo naturalis*) and artificial order (*ordo artificialis*). Natural order is that which arranges elements, as they would be presented in reality: either in a chronological sequence, following the ascending order of members of a set, or in causal order. Artificial order introduces its own contrived sequence, which distances itself from natural reality, with the aim of counteracting boredom in the audience. Although it may be useful in some cases, this order tends to diminish the credibility of the speech. Natural order is characteristic of scientific discourse, which routinely follows a logical structure. Herranz (1993: 77) points out that scientific discourse bases its well-structured order on three elements: the structuring into parts, the organised arrangement of the parts and the connection between them. The arrangement of the parts in an organised manner means putting each one in the place to which it logically corresponds.

This same criterion of logical organisation has also been proposed for audiovisual discourse dealing with news. According to Miller (180: 218), audiovisual news often follows logical models of organization, in which the facts are organised in ways which are: chronological, spatial, cause-effect, problem-solution, simple to complex, familiar to unknown, specific to general, general to specific or following a personal experience. These schemes are frequently used by popularisers. For example, David Attenborough organises his documentaries following some of these models. The series *Life on Earth* uses a chronological approach to organise the episodes within the series. However, in each of these episodes the facts are organised following the models of "general-specific" and "problem-solution". These same schemes are also used in his other series, both in the general structure and for each episode.

With regard to the subdivision of the speech into parts, rhetoric proposes various models. One of the most extensively discussed is the division into four parts, which seems particularly appropriate for forensic needs. According to this model, a speech begins with an introduction (*exordium*) that aims to stir the curiosity of the public; it is followed by the presentation of the facts (*narratio*) and the argumentation (*argumentatio*) of the specific point of view being presented and ends with a conclusion (*peroratio*).

Other models divide a speech into two or three parts. Bipartition is usually useful in cases where two opposing ideas are presented. The division into three parts distributes the overall discourse into a beginning, middle and end.

This tripartite model has been widely used within the documentary genre. Miller (1980: 219) recommends using this structure so that the introduction serves to situate the audience in the theme that will be dealt with, the middle develops the central theme and the end presents some type of result, which is normally a conclusion and review of the presentation of the basic premise.

Generally speaking, a division into three parts gives unity to the discourse, as it highlights the integrity of the whole. On the other hand, the absence of such a scheme seems to contribute to the sensation the viewer has that the set of elements lacks unity.

Verbal formulation is considered to be the most difficult and most important aspect of rhetoric, as it is verbal expression which decides the persuasive capacity of the ideas. Silverstone (1986: 92) distinguishes four rhetorical dimensions in documentaries: appearance, image, voice and music. Through the analysis of each of these and their interactions, it is possible to decipher the mechanisms by which a specific discourse manages to convince an audience. A detailed analysis of how these four dimensions are presented in scientific documentaries will not be undertaken here, as this subject is discussed, from different perspectives, in chapter 3. We will limit ourselves here to examining some aspects which are of special interest, in order to be able to understand how popularisers arrange the elements that comprise documentaries (words, images, and sounds).

As far as verbal language is concerned, rhetorical doctrine indicates that, in order to obtain an adequate *elocutio*, the speaker should bear in mind certain grammatical rules, which guarantee the correct use of language, and the rules of rhetoric, which make the persuasive effectiveness of the discourse possible. Among the most widely used criteria for composing a verbal commentary for a documentary is the need to be clear and precise, qualities that, as has been shown, coincide with those previously mentioned for successful popularisation.

Commentary is written in order to be heard, and so it seems appropriate that it should adopt a conversational tone. According to Boswall (1974: 44), this means that the grammatical rules which control written language need not necessarily be applied to a commentary in a documentary. For example, it is sometimes better to alter the natural order of a phrase so that a better effect is achieved when it accompanies images.

Documentary producers accept that, in general, the commentary should focus on that which the images alone cannot communicate. Boswall (1974: 44) specifies that, in some documentaries, the commentary usually serves to identify the living beings that appear in the images, explain their behaviour, express an aesthetic appreciation, introduce an element of humour and contribute to the unity of the programme.

Of the classical criteria for effectiveness of persuasion, the subject of the variety of discourse (*variatio*) is especially important. Rhetorical doctrine designates with this term the set of resources whose aim is to achieve variety in the thread of ideas and in their elocutionary expression, thus avoiding boredom in the audience. Although science usually constitutes an interesting and varied subject, on occasions it is necessary to reinforce these qualities, so in these documentaries use is made of a wide variety of images.

In some cases it is possible to increase variety in a documentary by combining *voice over* narration with on camera shots of the narrator. This resource is used in many programmes, where the combination of a *voice over*, excerpts of an interview and on screen presence of the narrator imbue the discourse with a certain degree of narrative variety. Furthermore, the introduction of music in some scenes also contributes to widening the variety of the programme. In the programmes analysed for this study, music is used sporadically, because if it were to be used throughout the programme it would lose its effect. This criterion of use is adhered to in the majority of documentaries, because if music is used for any length of time the viewer ceases to hear it.

Music in nature documentaries becomes an element that helps to bring the subject closer to the dramatic and narrative forms that are familiar to the viewer. However, music is an element that can humanise the animals and plants that appear on screen. For this reason, some producers have tried to reduce to the absolute minimum the amount of music used, as it is thought that the programme can gain in quality precisely because it does not have music. In spite of this, music is a very useful element in the production of a documentary, as it serves to create emotional situations which would not be possible through commentary alone, such as tension, drama or suspense.

In all audiovisual discourse, the variety and wealth of the image is especially important. A documentary is visually rich when it is composed of attractive images that are capable of captivating the audience. Furthermore, where possible, the images should also be varied both in content and in the specific form the documentary maker decides on, for example, the size and movement of different shots. In some documentaries the scriptwriter and the producer have to make a tremendous effort to conceive and compile images which are appealing and striking. Documentaries and research reports, which have a lack of interesting images, have to rely on simple dramatisations, computer animation, or archive material in order to achieve appeal.

In some scientific documentaries, such as those dealing with nature, the subject itself of the discourse offers an image which is always attractive and interesting. In spite of this, the scriptwriter also has, in this case, a considerable margin in which to try to maximise the visual richness of the programmes. According to Attenborough (1994), the main criterion, which is used to write scripts, is to fit a logical succession of ideas onto the subject which is to be developed. Once this outline has been drawn, the scriptwriter also tries to maintain the visual interest, as it is the images that draw the initial response from the viewer. This is how he expresses it:

> The story line has to be followed but the form has to be kept in mind too. For example, starting and finishing with sequences that have a high visual impact and using rapid sequences followed by slower ones.

The on camera shots of the presenter run the risk of becoming static shots, with little visual interest, and lacking in the appeal of the other images that make up the programme. This risk can be avoided by giving the shots a certain degree of movement, having the presenter walk through a particular place or carry out eye-catching actions.

Within the formulation phase of the verbal discourse, rhetoric places special importance to the question of style (*stylus*). Style designates a set of lexical, syntactical, rhetorical and content characteristics of speech. Styles have been traditionally classified according to different criteria some of which originate from the adaptation of the elements of speech among themselves (*aptum interno*). According to these criteria, expression should be appropriate for the theme being dealt with in such a way that a formal theme implies an elevated style and a modest or trivial theme a low style. From here comes the distinction between styles: low (*humilis*), middle (*medius*) and elevated (*grandiloquus*). Programmes that use a low style use, as a result, predominantly simple language, almost colloquial, which is tremendously usefully in popularisation, as it facilitates their intelligibility and their acceptance by the public.

4.4 Argumentation through the Qualities of the Narrating Subject

Having examined some of the issues relating to the process of production, we now turn to the study of the rhetorical arguments that are usually used in science documentaries. This study is carried out following the classical rhetorical model, which divides rhetorical resources, whether they be signs, arguments or examples, according to the three fundamental elements of any communicative situation: the speaker, the listeners and the speech itself.

The first type of argument, of an ethical nature, aims to provide proofs which allow the speaker to appear to be worthy of the public's trust. This set of forms of argumentation is based on an idea that Aristotle (*Rhetoric* I, 1356) expresses in the following terms: "we believe decent people more and sooner, and about anything in general, even about uncertain things that are doubtful". Argumentation through the virtues of the speaker is more useful in a debate; however, to a greater or lesser extent, the image of a speaker influences the capacity of argumentation in any of the other elements of a communicative situation.

The television documentary assigns the presenter with a prominent role. The presenter's on screen appearances normally act as the backbone of the structure of the programme. Furthermore, the fact that presenters become well-known figures increases their credibility in the eyes of the public. There is a natural presumption of credibility, as the first reaction of a listener is to accept as true what he/she hears. In the case of information which is transmitted through the mass media, the audience tends to trust the presenter will not misinform them. It is clear that this presumption of veracity can be reinforced when the speaker is someone already well known.

The requirement that the speaker, whether reporter or presenter, be ethically qualified is especially relevant for those working in the field of television news. Given that the television "speakers" habitually adopt the role of someone who reasons calmly and disinterestedly, they can only fulfil their role if their moral reputation is not tainted in any way. In this context, it is no surprise that, as Nichols (1991: 135) points out, the public expects presenters to lead "exemplary lives".

Classical rhetoric recommends speakers to aim to give the best impression of themselves as people, in order to gain the audience's respect, good will and sympathy. Nowadays, the prestige surrounding science and its methods of analysis seems to have diminished the effectiveness of argumentation that is not made through discourse itself. However, the following observation by Quintiliano (in Perelman, 1989: 489) is still valid today: "it is often the case that the same language is free in one speaker, foolish in another, and arrogant in a third". Some sources of information, individual or collective, are characterised by their credibility, while others do not share the same features. It seems clear, then, that the speakers themselves and the image shown to the public influence their capacity of argumentation, given that the viewers are more inclined to accept arguments from those who they consider to be worthy of trust.

As Reinard (1991: 353) points out, for many people it is difficult to separate the person from the words or arguments they use. Therefore, credibility is not additional to an argument; but rather it interacts with it. According to Aristotle, (*Rhetoric* II, 1378 a) speakers are worthy of trust for three reasons: prudence, virtue, and benevolence. Prudence (*fronesis*) is present in speakers that "consider correctly"; virtue, or lack of evil (*arete*), allows them to say, "what they think". Finally, benevolence is the capacity to look "with good will" to give good advice.

Reinard (1991: 353–354) distinguishes between two basic dimensions of the speaker's credibility: character and competence. Character is the degree to which the speaker is perceived as worthy of trust, therefore it seems safe to trust in people who have a good reputation. Competence, the more important of these two basic dimensions, is the degree to which the speaker is perceived to be knowledgeable about, or an expert in the subject.

In epideictic speech the speaker can rely on, at least initially, the audience's attention, because of the allusions to principles or values that are widely accepted. However, in this genre more than in any other, the speaker should have an excellent reputation and should be qualified for dealing with the subject in hand.

Roqueplo (1983: 126) points out that the scientific populariser, like the sports reporter, does not have the problem of trust that, for example, a political reporter would have. What the populariser tells us is accepted as "the Truth with a capital letter". This ready willingness on the part of the public seems to be related to the fact that popularisation is constructed through epideictic speech and to the manner in which the presenter transmits the message.

With regard to trust, it should be borne in mind that on television (and all popularisation discourse, in general), there is nothing which is equivalent to footnotes. Some see in this fact a reinforcement of the presenter's authority, as it seems that agreeable presenters have invented the knowledge they are talking about. However, the knowledge that the presenter-populariser is transmitting to the public usually comes from scientists, who are specialists in the field in question. This can be attested to in the list of acknowledgements which are included in the credits of nearly all programmes. In other words, the presenter acts with an authority which, in certain regards, has been borrowed from scientists.

The fact that scientific sources are not cited, even as an argument in the case for authority, is routine practice in science documentaries. The immediate consequence is that the public may perceive the presenter to be the sole source of information on the subject.

In addition to the two basic dimensions already mentioned, Reinard (1991: 361) distinguishes three auxiliary dimensions of the speaker's credibility: serenity, sociability and extroversion. When speakers are serene, the public perceives that they have control over their emotions and believe that the message will come across more easily. Sociability is based on the principle that the public is attracted by those speakers that seem friendly, as they consider their opinions on certain themes to be convincing. Finally, extroversion is the degree to which the speaker is projected outwards and is filled with dynamism. It is the characteristic which is attributed to those who speak in a lively manner, avoiding boring and monotonous speech.

In some cases, an excessively extroverted style can affect the serenity of the speaker and, as a result, their credibility. This occurs when the speaker gives the impression of having lost control. According to Pradines (in Perelman, 1989: 61), an enthusiastic speech, while capable of having some effect, does not seem to be authentic, because the emotional reality "bores holes into the mask of logic". Furthermore, an enthusiastic speaker tends to think that the arguments that convinced him or her will also convince their audience.

It is no surprise that the presenter of a documentary moves, with complete freedom, through time and space. Some programmes are set solely in the present, unconcerned that the actions which are broadcast were filmed over a number of days, months or years. To be able to present this narrative in the present, the presenter should appear in situations that took place at different times, with the aim that all of them should be seen as close together in time as possible. To this continuity in time, a contribution is made by the audiovisual discourse which these documentaries use, in which the mention of the passing of time is rarely made, whether this be verbal (explicit allusions in the text) or visual (with transitions such as fade to black or mixings). Other visual elements also contribute to this timelessness, such as the clothing worn by the presenter, which is usually the same or very similar in all the on screen shots. This timeless present contributes to the increase of the degree of imitation of reality (mimesis), as it distances viewers from the narrative and draws them closer to the representation. In this way, the theatrical effect is that actions which are shown in the present seem closer to the viewer.

4.4.1 On-camera statements

Some science documentaries feature on-camera statements by the presenter. David Attenborough (1994) believes that each one of these should be justified, given that on seeing the presenter the public probably asks itself "why is he getting in the way?" According to this criterion, the main reasons for including the on-camera statements by the presenter are varied. First, clothing and way of speaking can provide information about the temperature or the environment where the shot is filmed. For example, if it is hot or cold or if the presenter feels comfortable. Second, it can also serve to give information on the size of the objects or organisms that are featured. Third, the statements serve to generalize ideas that would otherwise be attributed to one specific animal. Finally, they can be used to start and end the chapters or sections that make up a programme.

Once it has been decided to include this type of presentation on screen, the aim is that the result should be as interesting as possible. This is achieved by filming the presentations in places that offer the widest possible visual appeal. Generally speaking, these are filmed in places where the events that are narrated actually took place, which also has a direct relevance on the credibility of the message. This technique, frequently used in television news reporting, has been highlighted by Vilarnovo and Sánchez (1992: 90).

> In audiovisual news reports the aim is, often, to give the sensation of reality using as the set the place in which the events presumably took place: in this case scenes are as well prepared as those in the theatre or in indoor studios, with the function of truthfulness.

Among many other examples of Attenborough's famous on-camera statements, one of his series *Life in the Undergrowth* (2005) can be highlighted. In episode 5, he climbs to the top of a tree, to watch a colony of giant bees. The manner of the presenter close to the insects can communicate, in a very effective way, the idea that giant bees can be very dangerous to human beings and the way they protect the colony.

To a certain extent, it can be said that the work of presenters is similar to that of actors, in that they play a role in front of the camera and what they say, in the majority of cases, they have learnt by heart. It is by no means easy, given that often during filming it is not clear which shots will be used before or after the shot being filmed. Furthermore, to this one has to add possible technical errors of diction or unexpected interference. Therefore, it may be necessary to repeat a shot several times, for which reason it is clear that in the work of the presenter there is a certain degree of acting.

4.4.2 Forms of Non-verbal Argumentation

Although the line that separates verbal from non-verbal communication is blurred, the latter is generally considered to be a set of signs that are not expressed through words, but that form part of the communicative process and carry some meaning. These signs have been classified according to several criteria. According to Knapp (1992: 17–32), the following categories can be distinguished: 1) Body movement or kinaesthetic behaviour such as: gestures, body movements, facial expressions, eye movements or posture. 2) Physical characteristics: body type; for example, height, weight or colour of skin. 3) Tactile behaviour: caresses, blows or guiding the movements of others. 4) Paralanguage: voice qualities, laughter, tears and yawns. 5) Proxemics: perception of personal and social space 6) artefacts; for example: perfume, clothing or glasses. 7) Environmental factors: furniture, architectural style, lighting, colours or temperature.

A detailed analysis of all the types of non-verbal communication which are used in science documentaries would take us from the aim of the present study. It is enough to simply highlight some aspects related to the type of language used by presenters, their quality of voice, proximity and clothing. With regard to the language used by presenters, in the past, it was generally found to be within the range of standard English, (Received Pronunciation or BBC English in the UK and General or Standard American also known as Network English in the USA), which was the norm on television and radio. Aside from other argumentative considerations, it seems clear that the mastery of this norm had an effect on the presenter's credibility as narrator.

The good use of a standard version of a language has been highlighted by studies such that by Burgoon and Saine (in Reinard, 1991: 182), who state that audiences consider standard language to be more believable than regional dialects. This preference seems to be based on the belief that a speaker who has an accent or uses a regional dialect is different to the viewers, who do not identify themselves with this type of language, differences which distance the presenter from the general criteria. Furthermore, the quality of the voice contributes to strengthening the credibility of the language. It is not unusual for broadcasters and presenters to use a deep tone of voice which, according to the studies by Brown and others (in Reinard, 1991: 385), is the most preferred by the public. With regard to regional accents the BBC, in particular, has pioneered the use of presenters with regional accents, which are now generally accepted.

Issues dealing with proxemics have a degree of importance for any television presenter given that, for example, the size of the shot that appears on screen is not established arbitrarily. Studies dealing with the concept of proximity generally begin with the concept of territoriality, which is accepted by the majority of scientists specialising in human behaviour. This concept supports the theory that man has a certain personal space, the invasion of which is uncomfortable, if not intimidating. It is according to this space that normal, conversational distance is established. Studies carried out by various authors suggest that, in this conversational distance, there are various variables which can influence it, such as age, gender, ethnic and cultural backgrounds of the subject being discussed. Other research shows that closeness is interpreted as a sign that the speaker likes the audience or is drawn to it. However, when a certain point of proximity is exceeded the audience feels that its personal space has been invaded, which produces anxiety (see, for example, Knapp and Hall, 2002).

The criterion used by the BBC for the production of news or documentary programmes is to use, preferably, a medium close-up for the majority of interviews and on-camera statements by presenters. According to this criterion, the medium shot is normally used to introduce characters, while the close-up is reserved for those moments which require a greater intimacy with the audience.

The clothing worn by speakers is also considered to be a factor which affects their credibility. The clothes which are worn and the image which they give can influence the impression formed by the audience, especially with regard to reputation and competence.

4.5   Argumentation directed at the Audience's Disposition

The second group of rhetorical resources is made up of those which are aimed at establishing a rapport with the audience. In order to argue efficiently, what should be borne in mind is not so much what the speaker considers to be important or true, but rather the point of view of the audience. Recalling a comparison made by Baltasar Gracian, Perelman (1989: 61) says that some speeches are "like a feast where the dishes are prepared not according to the cook's taste but according to the taste of the guests".

The audience is the determining factor when deciding on the type of argumentation to be used in a speech. It is clear that a speaker will use different arguments if addressing an audience of scientists, who are specialists in their fields, compared to a television programme aimed at the general public. With regard to this point, which considers the mood of the audience, Aristotle states:

> Since what conforms to nature is pleasant, and those that are alike conform to nature, all things of the same genus and similar almost always find pleasure among themselves, thus, man with man, horse with horse, youth with youth (*Rhetoric I,* 1371 b).

Rhetoric bears in mind this principle when it attempts to adapt messages according to the public. Using various means, the speaker can try to strengthen the sense of communion with an audience, looking for a ready willingness of the audience to accept what they hear. As Perelman (1989: 282–3) points out, it is frequent that this aim be carried out through references to common elements between the public and the audience, such as culture, tradition or history. When the speaker alludes to a fact or a custom, whose recognition distinguishes it as applied to a specific audience, the speaker is trying to establish a community of interests which will enable the message to reach the public effectively. Similarly, quotations, maxims or proverbs (aside from their primary function of reinforcing authority), aim to show that the speaker shares a certain cultural heritage with the audience.

The types of arguments which can be used vary, therefore, depending on the particular characteristics of the audience to which the speech is addressed. However, all speakers harbour the desire that arguments they use should be capable of transcending the local or historical peculiarities of a specific audience; that is to say, that what they seek is, ultimately, objectivity. According to Nichols, in the field of documentaries, the term objectivity has at least three aspects. The first aims to express that the documentary producer shows a world which is different to the one perceived by the actors or social agents; it deals with the point of view of someone who is independent. Second, objectivity implies that what is presented is a vision that is free of hidden agendas or prejudice. Finally, the intention of objectivity also presupposes that viewers are free to form their own opinions, basing them on the facts which are presented. That is to say, the aim is to avoid the type of argumentation associated with propaganda so that the viewers can form their own opinions freely.

If, in a discourse, use is made of argumentation, it is precisely because the evidence based on reality is not sufficiently strong, in itself, so as to convince the public. However, as García-Noblejas (1990: 61) points out, among the characteristics of argumentative communication is that which "opens the auditorium to the beat of uncertainty and, above all, the freedom to decide". Nonetheless, this freedom to decide cannot be complete, if the intention is to convince the public with a speech in which, in addition to objective facts, uses rhetorical arguments. Furthermore, it should not be forgotten that the audience does not become convinced solely through intellectual acceptance of a thesis but because its identification to the speech also implies emotional involvement. This idea was formulated by Aristotle (*Rhetorica* II, 1377 b), for whom the willingness of the audience decisively influenced the effectiveness of a speech, given that "it does not seem the same for those who feel love than those who feel hate, nor those who feel angry nor those who feel serene".

One of the basic criteria for judging the communicative efficiency of a science documentary is, precisely, its adaptation to the level of knowledge of the public. Popularisers know that their work has to adapt itself to the audience's understanding; David Attenborough (1994) expresses this in the following way:

> I tell stories or present facts in the way I would like to hear them myself if I didn't know anything about the subject. So what I do is be faithful to this approach and I try it out on myself.

And so the speaker aims to make the audience favourably disposed towards the speech so that, in this way, the objective of persuasion is more readily achieved. According to Quintilano (*Instituto Oratoria,* 12, 10, 59) this persuasion has three degrees, which he calls *docere, delectare, and movere. Docere* (teach) is the attempt to reach the spectator using evidence that appeals to the intellect; it is "the intellectual path to persuasion". The speech that aims to achieve appeals to the intellect but carries the danger of tedium (*taedium*), which is why it is necessary that it is accompanied by the second degree of persuasion: to delight (*delectare*), which seeks the sympathy of the public towards the speech and also towards the speaker. This sympathy is achieved by establishing an emotional bridge between the speaker and the public, appealing to the disposition of the soul (*ethos*) or by using humour (*ridiculum*). Rhetoricians and popularisers agree that humour is a very important factor when trying to convince an audience or, in general, when trying to establish a relationship between the speaker and the audience. In any speech, humour can be used with, at least, three objectives in mind: 1) to ease the tension and harshness produced by the emotional pressure exerted on the audience (*pathos*); 2) to divert attention which is too tense; 3) to lighten the spirit of the public and so make it more favourable.

The third degree of persuasion: to move (*movere*) produces a psychic shock in the audience so that it takes sides for the cause which the speaker is defending. This upheaval can be brought about by presenting the public with certain real objects (e.g. the victim's bloodstained clothing, in a judicial proceeding); or with mental and verbal resources that aim to accentuate the pathetic effects of the events (even if they are not pathetic *per se*). In audiovisual discourse, in principle, speakers do not need to present to the public real objects which produce an emotional effect, as they have at their disposal all the power of images in order to achieve this aim. Although some presenters do show objects when presenting on screen, it does not seem, however, that the aim is to emotionally involve the audience but rather to give visual richness to the shot.

4.6 Argumentation Through the Speech Itself

The third group of argumentative techniques are those that are based on the speech itself. In the case of the epideictic genre, the rhetorical resources which are used in the speech itself, take the form of praise of that which is beautiful or vituperation of that which is ugly. As Aristotle (*Rhetoric* I, 1368 a) affirms, "Praise is the most adequate form of for the demonstrative genre, since it assumes things have been already accepted by everyone so that the only thing necessary is to surround them with importance and beauty".

In fact, science documentaries, especially those dealing with nature, usually praise the beauty of living things and their actions, which are assumed to be in accordance with the laws of nature. Many are made following the model which is based on the structure of the classical documentary. This model, which we can consider to be the heir of Flaherty and of the British documentary movement, takes delight in the beauty of the images in the search for a balanced composition and the technical perfection of each shot. This conception implies, for example, the camera be always placed on a tripod or stable support. Using this set up, images are shot, repeating each shot as many times as necessary in order to meticulously adjust the composition with the camera angles. Some documentary producers, like Cousteau for example, have a style of filming that is more in keeping with movements such as in "direct cinema". In these programmes more importance is given to the spontaneity and freshness of the images than to formal beauty or balanced composition. For this reason filming is normally done with a "hand-held camera".

Within the classification of the modes of argumentation through speech itself, the question of *status* is particularly important. In the judicial genre *status* is the type of question that judges must ask themselves when facing the conflicting and contradictory statements of the two parties involved in a case. Given that, to some degree, all the genres are involved in the dialectic nature of this judicial genre, the classification of *status* of this genre can be applied to the other two. The central *status* of the epideictic genre is the *status qualitatis*, which has as its mission to rate the object according to its concord or discord with the law (Natural Law, Consuetudinary or Customary Law and Positive or Man-Made Law). Science documentaries generally try to praise the nobility of the actions presented, highlighting their concordance with natural law. On the other hand, they vituperate the anti-ecological behaviour of man, which goes against this law, as it destroys other living beings.

In the judicial genre, and to a certain extent in other genres, importance is given to the question of the increasingly difficult defensibility of a cause of *genus*, of which five can be differentiated: honest (*honestum*), dubious (*dubium*), admirable (*admirabile*), humble (*humile*) and obscure (*obscurum*). In the honest genre (*genus honestum*), the cause is totally justifiable, in accordance with the judicial sentiments of the public or with the general understanding of values and truth. And in the defence of an honest cause the dialectical element can take second place, giving way to an epideictic demonstration. This could be considered to be the case for documentaries, given that in them the public easily accepts the defensibility of the cause and, for the same reason, there is a predominance of the exaltation of the goodness and beauty of the subject of the speech – nature, scientific discovery, etc., with an almost total absence of an analysis of themes from opposing points of view. This dialectical approach is frequently found in documentaries dealing with political or social issues, that are usually controversial for the audience. However, in science documentaries, especially those dealing with nature, controversy or polemic is avoided, so that emphasis is placed on the praise of the object.

However, it must not be forgotten that the science documentary usually refers to matters that the public has little knowledge of, or which they consider to be of little importance. For this reason, popularisation is more similar to the humble genre, in which it is necessary for the speaker to make an effort to stir the public's curiosity and interest them in the subject.

4.7   Rhetorical Figures

Rhetorical figure is the name given to a rhetorical resource which is used in any type of argumentation. According to the classical definition, a figure is a conscious modification of normal common usage that carries an innovative artistic configuration. Following the classification established by Quintiliano and used by contemporaries like the academic research team called "Group μ", these modifications can be made in four ways: by addition (adiectio), omission (*detractio*), change of order (*transmutatio*) and substitution (*inmutatio*). Rhetorical operations based on substitution have traditionally received the name of tropes. The other three categories of modification serve as a basis for the figures themselves.

Throughout history, different terminologies and classification schemes have been proposed but their analysis exceeds the objectives of this study. Classical rhetoric distinguishes between figures of diction (*figurae elocutionis*) and figures of thought (*figurae sententiae*). The former affects linguistic expression itself, while the latter involve the conception of ideas. According to some authors, this subdivision can be confusing as, in fact, all the figures have simultaneous repercussions at the level of ideas and of expression.

Even though it is accepted that all rhetorical figures imply a simultaneous modification of form and content (or of thought and expression), the model which will be followed here is the classical scheme that separates the two types of figures. By following this model, it is possible to perform a more elaborate dissection of the most important rhetorical operations which are used by popularisers. Of the rhetorical operations used, those which most clearly affect popularisation are classified according to classical rhetoric as figures of thought. Using the same classical framework, the figures of thought can be subdivided into two groups: those that respond to the need to face the public and those that respond to the need to face the subject matter itself.

4.7.1 Figures facing the Public

The figures that arise when facing the public, serve the usefulness of the cause by intensifying the speaker's contact with the public. Figures used to face the public are of two types: those which use means of address and those that use questions. In the case of the former the speaker addresses the public in a special way, which consists, for example, of an insistent plea (*obsecratio*), a reproach to the audience (*licentia*) or abstention of address (*apostrofe*). In the case of the latter, the speaker addresses the public with questions.

Although addressing the public in a normal manner does not fall within the category of a figure, it should be remembered that in some documentaries, there are occasions where viewers are addressed directly, inviting them to observe images closely. These direct forms of address are related to what Perelman (1989: 282–5) terms figures of communion. It is with these that the speaker aims to interest the viewers, so they can actively participate in the speech thus increasing the community of interests with the audience.

Occasionally these direct forms of address take the form of questions. According to Lausberg (1996: 766), a question can be considered to be a rhetorical figure when "it is used in the speech, stripped of its true dialogical function, as a pathetic or especially expressive means of the cohesion of reasoning". Particularly useful are those that adopt the form of *subiectio*, with which the speaker begins a fictional dialogue, with questions and answers, with the aim of making the thread of reasoning livelier, so that the viewers can follow it more easily.

4.7.2 Figures dealing with the Subject Matter
The figures which arise as a result of the need of the speaker to face the subject matter, mainly affect the formation of the ideas themselves, and have a lesser effect on the intensification of contact with the public. These figures can be divided, on the one hand, into semantic, emotional and dialectic figures and on the hand, according to the four modifying categories (addition, omission, change of order and substitution).

Semantic figures affect meaning. They are operations related to what Perelman (1979: 278) terms figures "of presence" that aim to "keep in mind the subject matter of the speech". The basis of these figures is the definition (*finitio*), on which other rhetorical operations of this type are also based. The definition is a rhetorical figure in which significant and differentiating details to limit the concept or object concerned are indicated. The rhetorical definition does not, therefore, aim to clarify the meaning of a term but rather it aims to present to the audience certain aspects which would otherwise go unnoticed. The definition uses amplification through details that are partial ideas of a complete thought.

Another especially useful figure is antithesis (*anhtiteton*), which is used to compare two opposing ideas. Antithesis is a rhetorical operation used quite often by David Attenborough, above all to refer to behaviour that may surprise the audience. On occasions antithesis is used by taking as its basis information that may be unknown to the public. But this does not stop the comparison between the two ideas contributing to creating audience interest, assigning the behaviour being shown as characteristically anomalous or unusual. For example, in one sequence of the series *The Trials of Life* (episode VI, sequence 39), he refers to the behaviour of a snake as follows:

> Instead of laying eggs and abandoning them as most other snakes do, the female of this species becomes a mobile incubator; she retains the eggs inside her body to protect them and exposes them to the sun to keep them warm.

Other types of figures which are used to face the subject matter are the emotional ones. These are considered to be those figures that do not express real emotion, but which give a false impression of emotion using automated resources. These resources can arise as much from the confrontation of the speaker with the subject matter as with the public. Within the range of emotional figures, there is one that is especially important as a popularizing technique in science, for which reason it is the thread or scheme of argument around which the majority of programmes are produced. The term is *expolitio* (embellishment), a figure which consists of polishing and rounding off a thought by varying its elocutionary formulation and the supporting ideas related to the main idea. It is, therefore, an insistence on the main idea that is being presented.

Some documentaries follow similar schemes, focusing on one single central idea or on a few conceptually related ideas. As seen previously, in the section dealing with simplification, underlying the use of this rhetorical operation is the conviction of the screenwriter that television viewers do not take in too many ideas. It is therefore necessary to insist on one single idea, or a few key ideas and develop them in a unified way and in all their depth.

Some documentaries usually include some images which show, in detail, what has already been explained in the narration. These are moments in which the narrative is interrupted, so that the viewer can contemplate the images and listen to the music that usually accompanies them.

Another emotional figure that often appears in this type of documentaries is evidence (*evidentia*). This is a rhetorical operation based on a lively, detailed description of an object, based on enumerating its appreciable characteristics. The aim of a detailed description can be a procedure or, in the case of epideictic speech, people and things. Evidence aims to make the speech clearer and more credible. It seeks, all in all, to put the viewer in a position similar to that of an eyewitness to the events which are presented, basing itself on the criterion of analysis of elements as mentioned by Aristotle (*Rhetoric* I, 1365 a), who states: "when broken down into parts the same things look bigger".

In the case of television programming, the possibilities of placing the viewer in the position of an eyewitness are, in principle, greater than in other types of discourse. It is not in vain that the viewer can see the events or, at least those aspects that show images and sound. However, audiovisual discourse, can describe the same event in more or less detail, by varying the framing of the shot. For example, a film director can choose a particular image by varying the degree of close up. Although there is this possibility, it is common for the narrative which accompanies the images in a documentary to use the rhetorical operation of evidence. This figure is generally used to transmit information that complements that given by the image and sounds.

In the documentaries by David Attenborough it is possible to see some cases in which this figure is used. For example, in one sequence of *The Private Life of Plants* (episode III, sequence 28) the narrative describes the colonies of sea gulls in the following terms:

> They are dirty, foul-smelling places, full of excrement, pieces
> of half-digested fish and carcasses scattered all over the place.
> All in all, it is a true paradise for flies and ants.

While the narrative pauses during this description, the images show a colony of sea gulls without focusing on the details given. In this case, the detailed visual description would have been less effective than the verbal one, as the elements that convert the colony into a dirty place are not easily identifiable using an image. On the other hand, a description using words is much clearer. Furthermore, the accumulation of details also helps viewers position themselves as an eyewitnesses. Furthermore, the narrative gives details like temperature and time of day, which the image alone cannot express.

Another interesting example of this figure appears in the first episode of BBC's *The Blue Planet* (2002). In the first sequence of this film the blue whale is described as follows:

> It is far bigger than even the biggest dinosaur. Its tongue weights as much as an elephant. Its heart is the size of a car and some of its blood vessels are so wide that you could swim down them.

The details which are given in a figure of evidence need not necessarily be historical or taken from reality; it is enough that they seem to be true. In view of this, it is easier to understand that there is a certain antagonism towards this rhetorical figure, as has been shown by some theorists on scientific popularisation. For example, Le Lionnais, (in Calvo Hernando, 1977: 123) warns against the false objectivity of those who "talk about what they see", because only talking about what one person has seen lays the person open to serious errors. Dorothy Nelkin (1990:123) criticises the excess information which some journalists give "to create the illusion of certainty and the belief that confusing situations are under control".

In addition to characterizing details, evidence can also be achieved by other means. One of the most frequent is the use of language in the present tense, even for subject matter that is not in the present. This *translatio temporum* is used in many documentaries and has as its objective to reinforce the clarity and truth of the narrative, in addition to stirring the emotions of the viewer.

Another figure which is close to that of evidence, and which is also used by Attenborough, is that of *sermocinatio* (simulated dialogue), which consists of modifying the functionality of the speech, in such a way that the author pretends "in order to characterize normal people, sayings, conversations, monologues, or the unexpressed thoughts of the corresponding people".

In some nature programmes, like *The Living Desert* by Walt Disney, words are put into the mouths of animals, clearly following the model of *fictio personae*. The concession of giving words to animals is often used in fables, but not so in nature documentaries. Putting words in the mouth of animals is an extreme form of anthropomorphism, which can imply the loss of credibility, because the programme is drawing nearer to poetic formulations, losing its function as scientific discourse.

Another of the emotional figures, which is frequently used when facing the subject matter, is the simile (*similitudo*). It consists of establishing a parallel between the matter being discussed and a reality taken from nature and from human life in general. The similes which are most often used serve to compare aspects of animal life with human life, mainly from the point of view of habitat and behaviour. In fact, scientists have often used similes to explain their theories and points of view. For example, Isaac Newton explained that "the Universe is like a giant clock". As mentioned earlier, this type of anthropomorphic similes are also used by other documentary producers, as a means of bringing animal reality closer to human experience and, therefore, increase viewer interest in the life of animals, or interest in certain facts as revealed science. In a sequence from *Life of Earth* about reptiles (episode 6, sequence 2), iguanas getting out of the water are said to fall on to the shore, "as an exhausted swimmer would do after a long crossing in freezing water".

Some of the comparisons are sustained throughout a sequence or even a programme. The episode of Attenborough's *The Living Planet* about oceans (number 11) compares the seas and the Earth, explaining that coral reefs are equivalent to jungles and certain areas of the bottom of the sea are like deserts.

The simile can be established according to three grades of cognition. The maximum grade is characterised by the well-worn connection between the comparative image and the object shown. At the other extreme, is the minimum cognitive grade which relates the object to aspects of human life that are not well understood by the majority of persons. The intermediate grade establishes connections which are not too hackneyed, with less common content. This last grade is the one most suitable to the needs of prose. In this way, it fulfils the objective of bringing a new reality closer to one the viewer is already familiar with, also contributing to the ornamental needs of the speech.

Especially useful in science communication is metaphor (*metaphora*); a figure in which a word or phrase is applied to something it does not literally resemble, in order to emphasise particular qualities. Sometimes a metaphor is used several times within a programme. For example, the third episode of *The Private Life of Plants* uses the metaphor of animals as "clients" of other animals: bees are clients of orchids, since they drink their nectar; and chaffinches are clients of tortoises, since they eat their parasites.

In some cases, a metaphor can adopt an extended form to become an allegory (*allegoria*). An excellent example can be found in the first episode of the documentary mini-series *The Elegant Universe* (2003), produced by Joe McMaster and Julia Cort for *Nova*. The theory of quantum mechanics is explained by the presenter (scientist Brian Greene) entering the "quantum café", a visual construction that allows the viewer to enter a "crazy world" governed by chance or probability, in which the normal rules of physics do not apply.

The figures derived from the dialectic nature of rhetoric are of special use in the judicial genre, as in this context the same state of affairs is always seen from two opposing points of view which correspond to the prosecution and the defence. In the epideictic genre, given that the opposing party never speaks, dialectic figures are less frequent.

This form of anticipating information, which will later serve the development of the speech (*semina spargere*), is frequently used in dramatic speeches. It is also important in some nature documentaries, especially those which adopt dramatic forms, such as those by Rodríguez de la Fuente.

As occurs with figures of diction, those related to thought can also be classified according to the four modifying categories of classical rhetoric (addition, omission, change of order and substitution). Some of the figures analysed in the previous sections could also be included in this category, as could some which will be studied in the following sections be included in previous ones.

Addition figures (*per adiectionem*) take as their basis "the addition of one or various elements that do not belong to the whole". Addition is directly at the service of amplification, for which reason is it especially useful in the epideictic genre, which revolves around the amplification of non-controversial subject matter.

One figure of addition which is used by popularisers is the sentence (*sentencia*). This is one infinite thought (that is to say, not limited to a specific case), formulated as a sentence and which is used in a specific matter (*quaestio finita*), as proof or as adornment (*ornatus*). It is also a thought formulated by common knowledge. As stated by Aristotle (Rhetoric I, 1394 a to 1395 b), the sentence does deal with any infinite question, but deals with action. Within the structure of Aristotelian rhetoric, the sentence is formed by the conclusion, the premise of an enthymeme, eliminating the syllogism. Sentences please listeners (especially listeners who are unsophisticated), because they generally express what they already specifically know. Furthermore, sentences bestow a moral character to the speech, which means that "if the sentences are good, they also make the speaker look good". Finally, the sentence serves the purpose of gathering the sense of all that has been said up to that moment and relaunching what comes next.

Figures of thought by detraction (*per detraction*) are carried out by the omission of ideas. They can have as their objective brevity (*percussion* and *postponement*) or the intention of being an emotional figure (reticence). In fact, all programmes are made on the basis of a "detraction" of all the content that does not exactly fit in with the narrative thread or sequence of ideas which is presented. However, this approach is not taken in operations which involve the explicit use of some the figures of detraction which characterise rhetoric. This is in regard to an approach which is used in the initial selection of the contents (*inventio*), rather than in the arrangement of the speech (*dispositio*). Furthermore, for some, this detraction of the content is practically consubstantial to audiovisual discourse, which seems unsuited to deal with subjects in any depth.

Figures of transmutation (*per transmutation*) coordinate two lines of thought. Within this category is meta-thesis (*hysterologia*), which consists of coordinating two types of content reversing their natural order. That is to say, it consists of changing the order which takes places in the normal course of events (*ordo naturalis*) for another which is different (*ordo artificialis*). The majority of documentaries follow a natural order, given that the narrative thread is generally based on a logical succession of ideas which go from the general to the specific; one of the forms of natural order which characterises rhetoric. This order is especially appropriate for epideictic speech, in which the cause presents favourable signs of defence.

Another of the figures used with some frequency is hyperbole (*hyperbole*), which consists of an intentional exaggeration which is used with the aim of creating a momentary poetic effect. It can be executed by gradual intensification, simile, comparison, sign or metaphor. Examples of this figure, found in Attenborough's work are expressions like "a mountain of flesh", when referring to the whale (*Life on Earth*, episode X, sequence 16) and "walking zoo", referring to the buffalo and its multitude of parasites (*The Trials of Life*, episode VII, sequence 20). These figures fulfil, firstly, a function similar to that of evidence, by making the subject of the speech present in the mind of the viewer. Furthermore, hyperbole has a humorous effect which, as has been seen, favours the engagement with the audience.

Conclusions

The popularisation of scientific knowledge aimed at the general public should bridge the gap that separates scientific knowledge from common knowledge. To do this, it is necessary to develop a specific type of formulation, in which scientific knowledge undergoes a process of adaptation to the ways in which the public, to whom the formulations are addressed, understand concepts.

Communicative effectiveness by some popularisers is based on a series of techniques and habits which make the message more attractive and intelligible. It would be simplistic reductionism to state that just by using these resources, the effectiveness of the popularisation of scientific content can be assured. In the communication of knowledge, which is specific to science and addressed to the general public, a large number of elements of a diverse nature play a part, which convert this activity into one of the most complex in the sphere of communication. For this reason, even though the techniques which have been identified in the present study may be generally useful, the populariser should bear in mind the specific elements of each discipline and of the communicative situation.

A good work of popularisation stands out because of its capacity to adapt the scientific content to the interests and ways of understanding of the general public. Although some science documentaries deal with, in principle, subjects which are outside the sphere of interest of the public, it is possible to relate this content to elements of the everyday experiences of the public, in such a way that the two realities are brought closer together. This rapprochement is particularly important given that science as such, does not usually appear in the range of common interest of the public. Therefore establishing this relationship between an unknown reality (scientific knowledge) and one that is known (everyday experience) becomes one of the key elements to be borne in mind in the transmission of scientific knowledge to the layman.

In the attempt to bring science closer to the reality which is familiar to the public, there is a danger that the formulation loses scientific rigor, as a result of using models that are easily understood, but that do not correspond to reality. However, intelligibility and scientific rigor are concepts that are not mutually exclusive. On the contrary, one of the characteristics which distinguishes the work of good popularisers is that their work transmits, with rigour, scientific knowledge which has been contrasted by leading experts.

In order to bring the public closer to knowledge taken from science, documentaries use a series of techniques and communicative forms which comprise useful models for the popularisation of scientific knowledge. In order to capture the attention of the viewer, it has been shown to be effective to make references to aspects of reality that are unusual or strange. It would be difficult for these *unusual elements,* by themselves, to constitute a rigorous scientific formulation. However, when they are appropriately used within the narrative framework, they can be an element of additional interest which, furthermore, does not undermine the scientific rigour of the work as a whole. These elements also serve to rouse the curiosity of viewers, as a first step to gaining their admiration of science.

Documentaries often show exotic places on Earth and examples of animal and plant behaviour which are clearly outside the range of what is considered to be normal. As mentioned previously, the use of examples of this type does not necessarily diminish the scientific value of the programme, as these are always shown as an integral part of the weave of the storyline which highlights the principles accepted by science.

One of the key operations in a popularisation programme is the *simplification* of content. This simplification begins with establishing the *narrative thread* or central idea of each series and of each programme. Through this line of argumentation, it is possible to construct a programme that avoids the multiple ramifications which are characteristic of scientific discourse, and which brings the programme as a whole closer to the characteristics of a work of art.

In addition to the essential method of simplification using the sequencing of ideas, other means are also used, such as the *reduction of dimensions* to a scale that the mind of the viewer can easily take in. These reductions are appropriate for popularisation, as they give the viewer access to magnitudes of space and time which, in their true dimensions, would be difficult to assimilate.

The *suppression of controversy* is another way of simplifying reality, which is particularly suitable for certain science documentaries, especially those which deal with nature. In some discourses, it is possible to maintain interest by presenting opposing points of view. On the other hand, in other cases, by eliminating opposing ideas it is possible to help viewers, so that they can more easily understand the message that is being put across. This type of simplification process is appropriate for those subjects in which there is already an internal conflict, for example, animal behaviour – which is sufficient to keep the viewer interested.

It is clear that all popularisation programmes necessarily include some type of simplification. Furthermore, it should be remembered that some scientific subjects, due to their intrinsic complexity, are more difficult to popularise than others. Certain aspects of scientific knowledge are more easily communicated to the public, but this is not to say that the popularisation can only deal with subjects which are extremely simple. What it does imply, however, is the decisive role of popularisers in their capacity to create an effective broadcast.

A frequently used means of bringing the subject closer to the viewer is to attribute to it certain human traits that it does not, in fact, possess. In popularisation documentaries, *anthropomorphism* is both commonly used and at the same time reviled. However, it should be remembered that this technique constitutes, in fact, a general tendency of both language and knowledge, with which man aims to associate those realities which escape the boundaries of knowledge, with mental constructs that can be understood.

The use of this resource does not necessarily imply that scientific knowledge which is transmitted is distorted. The distrust that zoologists and documentary producers hold against anthropomorphism is the result, in good measure, of positions adopted by certain movements such as socio-biology or genetic determinism that apply the results of animal behaviour to the realm of human activity. However, it should be remembered that these types of approaches are not necessarily anthropomorphic.

To the narrative interest of the science documentary there is also the contribution made by the inclusion of certain *anecdotes* and other specific elements, by which the enjoyment of the documentary is increased. The use of this type of resource in popularisation has been criticised, as it has been considered that the knowledge derived from them lacks the necessary scientific rigor. However, these elements can be used sporadically, in such a way that the weight of the narrative does not rest on them and, therefore, there is no distortion of the meaning of the message, by raising the accessory to the category of the essential.

One way of adapting scientific knowledge to the way in which the public thinks is to use *dramatic structures*. However, the use of this resource in the popularisation of science can pose a number of problems. One of these is that which results from the reduction of fact and circumstances taken from the real world to categories which are easily intelligible and attractive but in the final analysis, false, e.g. heroes and villains. However, this danger can be avoided, on condition that the search for dramatic structures is not taken to the extreme of distorting reality, in order to adapt it to the aforementioned categories. It should be borne in mind that, when used correctly, dramatic techniques could be useful for popularizing science, as through them it is possible to present certain subjects to the public, in a way that is both interesting and intelligible.

From the range of dramatic techniques which can be used, the one which stands out most is that of organizing the contents around a story. It is preferable for these narratives to develop complete actions: that is to say, to have a beginning, middle and an end. Within them there is a re-creation of certain situations found in the real world, which contributes to the reinforcement of the credibility of the programme, for which reason the artificiality of the representation is less evident and viewers can be led to believe that they are watching reality itself and not its representation.

For these stories to develop, it is necessary that real beings be portrayed as characters which are involved in conflicts. Given that the *conflict* is an essential element to keep the interest of the viewer, it is much easier to popularise subjects in which conflict is present. For example, in the specific case of nature documentaries, numerous conflicts appear, given that living organisms are often involved in difficult situations.

When stories are told in which some characters have aims, it is also possible to create suspense in the documentary. This narrative element is extremely important as this keeps the interest of the viewer centred on what is being narrated. Generally speaking, suspense is possible in situations where there is a degree of uncertainty as to the final resolution of a conflict.

The transmission of scientific knowledge requires a strong bond to be established between the populariser and the audience which is being addressed. There are various means of intensifying this *community of interests*, which are related to some of the three elements found in all communicative situations: the formulating subject, the public and the discourse. Through these, popularisers aim to make the viewer believe that what they see is true and interesting.

Scientific popularisation can be classified within the epideictic rhetorical genre. In this genre, the audience is not asked to judge the matter which is presented, given that, because it deals with knowledge that is shared without any discord, they need only evaluate the aesthetic interest of the formulation. In accordance with their condition of epideictic discourse, documentaries find their main form of argumentation in the praise of beauty and goodness of the living organisms which comprise their subject.

In popularisation discourse, the opinion the public has of the speaker is of utmost importance. This opinion is based mainly on the ethical reputation of the speaker and the speaker's expertise in the field under discussion. The effectiveness of the narrative used in this type of documentary depends, to a large degree, on the speaker's credibility as narrator, which is reinforced by his or her moral reputation and knowledge of the subjects which are discussed.

The fact that in popularisation discourse no references are made to scientific sources means that the credibility of the programme falls on the presenter. For this reason, image and reputation are the deciding factors for the public's acceptance of this type of discourse. The presenter's image is also determined by other factors such as serenity, sociability and extroversion. The communicative effectiveness of a television presenter also depends on an appropriate balance between these elements.

The presenter's *on camera* shots are a deciding element to reinforce his or her credibility and, as a result, that of the programme. In these statements the importance of various forms of non-verbal argumentation are highlighted. Of particular importance are: the quality of the voice of the presenter, the fact that colloquial language is used, the type of shot in which the presenter appears and the clothes that are worn.

The effectiveness of popularisation discourse does not only depend on its intellectual capacity to transmit knowledge, but the degree to which the public accepts the speech, which also implies emotional considerations. It is therefore useful to use certain resources, aimed at obtaining a favourable predisposition of the audience towards the speech. To this end, popularisers use a number of techniques, such as the inclusion of humorous elements and spectacular images, through which they hope to stop the audience from getting bored and, as a result, have a positive attitude towards the documentaries.

The programme which is dedicated to the popularisation of scientific knowledge is closely related to the *humble genre* of classical rhetoric, in which the audience holds a neutral position on the subject which is presented. For this reason, it is particularly important that the populariser should know how to draw the audience's attention to the topics that are being communicated. Furthermore, the *natural order* is appropriate for popularisation discourse, as it presents a logical structure that contributes to the strengthening of its credibility, as a mechanism for the transmission of scientific knowledge.

The use of specific rhetorical figures contributes to the strengthening of the intelligibility of popularisation discourse, as it is through them that it is possible to adapt scientific knowledge to the audience's way of understanding. In this type of documentary, use is made of various operations, which are aimed at intensifying the contact between the formulating agent and the public.

In popularisation discourse certain rhetorical operations, which refer to the way in which the speaker deals with the subject matter, have been shown to be effective. Those which stand out are certain figures, which aim to facilitate the audience's interest in the subject of the speech. To this same end, are used certain *emotional figures* such as *expolotio,* evidence and *sermocinatio.* With these it is possible to make the discourse clearer and more credible, as the subject is developed in sufficient depth so that the image which is held in the audience's mind has all the necessary details. Other emotional figures which stand out are the *simile* and personification. The use of these make it possible to relate the subject of the discourse to the realities of human life, which enable the audience to understand more clearly the issues which are presented.

Some rhetorical operations which are also effective in the aim to achieve greater clarity in exposition are those which are carried out *by immutability,* or substitution of one main idea by a secondary one. Among these, those which stand out are the allegory and *hyperbole,* whose main function is to present an image through which the audience can understand the subject which is being dealt with more clearly.

Finally, in view of the considerations mentioned above, it should be borne in mind that scientific popularisation uses a specific type of discourse whose means and aims are not necessarily scientific. Popularisation discourse is not, strictly speaking, simplified scientific discourse, but is based on a type of discourse that has its own characteristics, with which it is possible to disseminate aspects of scientific knowledge, in such a way that it is interesting and comprehensible to the general public.

For this discourse to fulfil its aim, it is essential that the ideas which are presented keep the necessary scientific rigour, in such a way that the audience is able to access a sound understanding of reality. Therefore, it is necessary that the populariser use techniques that help to make the discourse interesting, credible and intelligible, provided that their use does not distort reality to the point where the discourse lacks the necessary scientific rigour.

The populariser must reach a delicate balance between faithfulness to the scientific discourse and an attempt to build a discourse, which is interesting for the lay public. In order to achieve this, science documentaries require the creation of a new type of discourse, rather than the simple translation of a scientific text to the public's language.

References

AGUINAGA, Enrique de (1987), *Programa de cátedra*, Madrid, Facultad de Ciencias de la Información, Universidad Complutense.

ARISTOTLE, *Rhetorics*, edited by GARCÍA YEBRA, Victor (1974), Madrid, Instituto de Estudios Políticos.

ARISTOTLE, *Poetics*, edited by GARCIA YEBRA, Víctor (1988), Madrid, Gredos.

ARRUTI, Alberto, "La divulgación científica como relato: Una aproximación a la ciencia-ficción", in BARRERA, Carlos and JIMENO, Miguel A. (eds.) (1991), *La información como relato: Actas de las V Jornadas Internacionales de Ciencias de la Información*, Pamplona, Servicio de Publicaciones de la Universidad de Navarra, pp. 407–415.

ATTENBOROUGH, David (1987), *The First Eden*, London, Collins.

___ (1994) Interview with the author, London, July 14th.

___ (1997) Interview with the author, London, March 7th.

BARSAM, Richard M. (1974), *Nonfiction Film*, Londres, George Allen and Unwin Ltd.

___ (1988), *The Vision of Robert Flaherty: The artist as Myth andFilmmaker*, Bloomington, Indiana University Press.

BARTHES, Roland (1994), *El susurro del lenguaje,* Barcelona, Paidos.

BERGER, Arthur (1990), *Scripting for Radio and Television*, London, SAGE Publications Ltd.

BETTETINI, Gianfranco (1995), "La divulgazione della scienza", in *Documenti di laboro* 60.

BOSWALL, Jeffery (1968), "An Interview with the Master: Heinz Sielmann answers questions", in *SFTA Journal* 32–33, pp. 38–44.

___ (1974), "Private Lives", in *EBU Review*, vol. XXIV, n. 6, pp. 36–45.

___ (1993), "Story-lines and links for biological moving imaging", lecture at the University of Derby (UK), unpublished.

BOUSÉ, Derek (2000), *Wildlife Films*, Philadelphia, University of Pennsylvania Press.

___(1995), "True Life Fantasies: Storytelling Traditions in Animated Features and Wildlife Films", in *Animation Journal 3(2)*, pp.19–39.

___ (1997), "What is a wildlife film", in *Diffusion*, summer, pp. 2–4.

BRAJNOVIC, Luka (1979), *El ámbito científico de la información,* Pamplona, Eunsa.

BULHOFF, Ilse (1992), *The Language of Science*, Leiden, E. J. Brill.

CALVO HERNANDO, Manuel (1977), *Periodismo científico,* Madrid, Paraninfo, (2ªnd ed. 1992).

CHOZA, Jacinto (1982), "Unidad y diversidad del hombre, antropología versus metafísica", in *Revista española de pedagogía* 158, pp. 15–25.

CHOZA, Jacinto (1988), *Manual de antropología filosófica*, Madrid, Rialp.

CONSIDINE, Mary Lou (1986), "Wake up! It's Science", in *Metro*, n. 71, primavera, p. 42.

COPPENS, Yves (1994), "Del austrolopithecus a la conquista del espacio", in *Label France* 17.

CROWTHER, Barbara (1994), lecture at simposium *Wildscreen '94*, Bristol (United Kingdom), unpublished.

DRICKAMER, Lee et al. (1992), *Animal Behaviour. Mechanisms, Ecology and Evolution*, Dubuque (IA), W. C. Brown Publishers.

DROUIN, Jean-Marc (1992), "Animalité et anthropomorphisme dans la diffusion et la vulgarisation scientifiques", in *Revue de synthèse* 3–4, pp. 333–345..

DUNNE, Philip (1946), "The Documentary and Hollywood", in *Hollywood Quarterly* 1(2), pp. 100–108.

ELLIS, Jack (1989), *The Documentary Idea*, Englewood Cliffs (New Jersey), Prentice Hall.

FALKUS, Hugh (1976), "Writing for wildlife films", in *BKSTS Journal*, June, pp. 168–172.

FERNANDEZ-RAÑADA, Antonio (1995), *Los muchos rostros de la ciencia*, Oviedo, Ediciones Nobel.

FELDMAN, Simón (1990), *Guión argumental, guión documental*, Barcelona, Gedisa.

FERNÁNDEZ DEL MORAL, Javier and ESTEVE RAMÍREZ, Francisco (1994), *Fundamentos de la información periodística especializada*, Madrid, Síntesis.

FLESCH, Rudolf (1960), *How to Write, Speak and Think More Efficiently*, New York, New American Library.

FORSTER, Edward M. (1983), *Aspectos de la novela*, Madrid, Debate.

GENETTE, Gerard (1989), *Figuras III,* Barcelona, Lumen.

GARCÍA-NOBLEJAS, Juan J. (1982), *Poética del texto audiovisual,* Pamplona, Eunsa.

___ (1988),"Fundamentos para una iconología audiovisual", in *Comunicación y sociedad* 1(1), pop. 21–71.

___ (1990), "Modos informativos, modos argumentativos", in GARCÍA-NOBLEJAS, Juan J. and SANCHEZ ARANDA, José J. (eds.), *Información y persuasión: Actas de las III Jornadas Internacionales de Ciencias de la Información*, Pamplona, Servicio de Publicaciones de la Universidad de Navarra, pp. 43–93.

___ (1996), *Comunicación y mundos posibles*, Pamplona, Eunsa.

GOULD, Stephen (1992), "La rueda de la fortuna y la cuña del progreso", in PRETA, Lorena, *Imágenes y metáforas de la ciencia*, Madrid, Alianza Editorial.

GRIERSON, John (1966), HARDY, Forsyth (ed.), *Grierson on Documentary*, Berkeley, University of California Press.

HERRANZ, Gonzalo (1993), "Cualidades y defectos", in VILARROYA, O. (ed.), *Manual de estilo. Publicaciones biomédicas,* Barcelona, Doyma, pp. 67–96.

IDROVO, Sandra (1991), "El dectective, analista y descubridor: narración, conflicto y fórmulas del relato en 20/20", in BARRERA, Carlos y JIMENO, Miguel (eds.), *La información como relato: Actas de las V Jornadas Internacionales de Ciencias de la Información*, Pamplona, Servicio de Publicaciones Universidad de Navarra, pp. 613–631.

INGARDEN, Roman (1968), *Vom Erkennen des Llitterarisken Kunstwerks,* Tübingen, Max Niemeyer Verlag.

JIMÉNEZ ALEIXANDRE, María P. (1995), "Divulgación y medio ambiente", in *Política científica* 42, pp. 45–48.

JONKEL, Charles (1985), "Never Cry Farley: A Treatise on Wildlife Fact and Fancy in Film and Novel", en *BKSTS Journal*, vol. LXVII, n. 3, March, pp. 104- 106.

KNAPP, Mark L. (1992), *La comunicación no verbal. El cuerpo y el entorno*, Barcelona, Paidós, 1992.

KNAPP, Mark L. And HALL, J. A. (2002), *Nonverbal communication in hunan interaction*, 5th edition, Belmont, CA: Wadsworth.

LANGLEY, Andrew (1985), *The Making of the Living Planet*, Londres, George Allen and Unwin.

LAUSBERG, Heinrich (1966), *Manual de retórica literaria*, Madrid, Gredos.

LÁZARO CARRETER, Fernando (1977), "El lenguaje periodístico, entre el literario, el administrativo y el vulgar", in VVAA, Lenguaje en periodismo escrito,

Madrid, Fundación Juan March, pp. 11–12.

___ (1980), "El mensaje literal", en *Estudios de lingüística*, Barcelona.

LÓPEZ PAN, Fernando (1997), "Consideraciones sobre la narratividad de la noticia. El imperio de una sinécdoque", in *Comunicación y sociedad*, vol. X, n. 1, pp. 9–60.

LYOTARD, Jean F. (1984), *La condición postmoderna: informe sobre el saber,* Madrid, Cátedra.

LLANO, Alejandro (1991), *Gnoseología,* Pamplona, Eunsa.

MARTÍN MUNICIO, Ángel (1986), "El nivel científico y tecnológico español es superior a lo que reflejan nuestros medios de comunicación", in *Fundesco* 62, pp. 5–7.

MARTIN PEREDA, José A. (1995), "De cómo llevar a cabo la divulgación científica", in *Política científica* 42, pp. 14–18.

MARTINEZ ALBERTOS, José L. (1989), *El lenguaje periodístico*, Madrid, Paraninfo.

___ (1992)., *Curso general de redacción periodística*, Madrid, Paraninfo.

MC CARTNEY, Hunter (1987), "Applying Fiction Conflict Situations to Analysis on News Stories", in *Television Quarterly* 64, pp. 163–170.

MCINTYRE, Alasdair (1987), *Tras la virtud*, Barcelona, Crítica.

MILLER, William (1980), *Screenwriting for Narrative Film and Television*, New York, Hastings House.

MUÑOZ TORRES, Juan R. (1991), "El interés como factor de configuración de la narración", in BARRERA, Carlos and JIMENO, Miguel A. (eds.), *La información como relato: Actas de las V Jornadas Internacionales de Ciencias de la Información*, Pamplona, Servicio de Publicaciones

Universidad de Navarra, pp. 195–212.

___ (1996), *El interés informativo*, Madrid, Fragua.

NELKIN, Dorothy (1990), *La ciencia en el escaparate*, Madrid, Fundesco.

NICHOLS, Bill (1991), *Representing Reality: Issues and Concepts in Documentary*, Bloomington, Indiana University Press, 1991.

NUÑEZ LADEVEZE, Luis (1991), *Manual para periodismo*, Barcelona, Ariel.

PANCORBO, Luis (1986), *La tribu televisiva. Análisis del documentaje etnográfico*, Madrid, IORTV.

PERELMAN, Chaïm (1979), *The New Rhetoric and its applications*, Dordrechts, D. Reisel.

PERELMAN, Chaïm and OLBRECHTS-TYTECA (1989), L., *Tratado de la argumentación. La nueva retórica*, Madrid, Gredos.

PIEPER, Josef (1988), *Las virtudes fundamentales*, Madrid, Rialp.

PRETA, Lorena (1993), *Imágenes y metáforas de la ciencia*, Madrid, Alianza Editorial.

QUINTERO MEZA, Ricardo (1991), "El protagonista en el relato periodístico", en BARRERA, Carlos y JIMENO, Miguel A. (eds.), *La información como relato: Actas de las V Jornadas Internacionales de Ciencias de la Información*, Pamplona, Servicio de Publicaciones Universidad de Navarra, pp. 391–404.

RAICHVARG, Daniel and JACQUES, Jean (1991), *Savants et ignorants. Une histoire de la vulgarisation des sciences*, Paris, Seuil.

REINARD, John (1991), *Foundations of Argument. Effective Communication for Critical Thinking*, Dubuque (IA), Wm. C. Brown Publishers.

REYES, Alfonso (1961), "Aristóteles o la teoría de la persuasión", in *Obras completas*, México, Fondo de Cultura Económica, vol. XIII.

RODRIGUEZ ADRADOS, Francisco (1979), *Historia de la fábula greco-latina*, Madrid, Editorial de la Universidad Complutense.

ROQUEPLO, Philippe (1983), *El reparto del saber: Ciencia, cultura, divulgación*, Barcelona, Gedisa.

ROTHA, Paul et al. (1970), *Documentary Film*, Nueva York, Hastings House Publishers.

SILVERSTONE, Roger (1985), *Framing Science: the Making of a BBC Documentary*, London, BFI.

___ (1986), "The Agonistic Narratives of Television Science", en CORNER, John (ed.), *Documentary and the Mass Media*, Londres, Edward Arnold Publishers, pp. 81–106.

THOM, René (1992), "La ciencia y el sentido", en PRETA, Lorena (ed.), *Imágenes y metáforas de la ciencia*, Madrid, Alianza Editorial.

TODOROV, Tzvetan (1977), *Théories du symbole*, Paris, Seuil.

TORANZO, Gloria (1968), *El estilo y sus secretos*, Pamplona, Eunsa.

TRATCHMAN, L. E. (1981), "The Public Understanding of Science Effort", in *Science, Technology and Human Values* 8, pp. 10–15.

TRUFFAUT, François (1974), *El cine según Hitchcock*, Madrid, Alianza Editorial.

TUDGE, Colin (1994), "Putting the God in Cod", in *The Independent on Sunday*, July 31st, p. 19.

VALE, Eugene (1992), *Técnicas del guión para cine y televisión*, Barcelona, Gedisa.

VILARNOVO, Antonio y SÁNCHEZ, José F. (1992), *Discurso, tipos de texto y comunicación*, Pamplona, Eunsa.

WARREN, Carl (1959), *Modern News Reporting*, New York, Harper & Brothers.

WYATT, Will (1983), "Documentary Programmes on Television. A Paper for the BBC General Advisory Council", London, BBC.

ZOHAR, Danah (1995), "Black Holes", in *The Sunday Times*, April 2nd, pp. 10–13.

ZUNZUNEGUI, Santos (1989), *Pensar la imagen*, Madrid, Cátedra/ UPV.

BASIC BIBLIOGRAPHY

BARSAM, Richard M. (1974), *Nonfiction Film*, Londres, George Allen and Unwin Ltd.

CALVO HERNANDO, Manuel (1977), *Periodismo científico*, Madrid, Paraninfo.

FELDMAN, Simón (1990), *Guión argumental, guión documental*, Barcelona, Gedisa.

FERNANDEZ DEL MORAL, Javier y ESTEVE RAMIREZ, Francisco (1994), *Fundamentos de la información periodística especializada*, Madrid, Síntesis.

GARCÍA-NOBLEJAS, Juan J. (1982), *Poética del texto audiovisual,* Pamplona, Eunsa.

HERRANZ, Gonzalo (1993), "Cualidades y defectos", in VILARROYA, O. (ed.), *Manual de estilo. Publicaciones biomédicas*, Barcelona, Doyma, pp. 67–96.

LAUSBERG, Heinrich (1966), *Manual de retórica literaria*, Madrid, Gredos.

MUÑOZ TORRES, Juan Ramón (1996), *El interés informativo*, Madrid, Fragua.

NELKIN, Dorothy (1990), *La ciencia en el escaparate,* Madrid, Fundesco.

NICHOLS, Bill (1991), *Representing Reality: Issues and Concepts in Documentary*, Bloomington, Indiana University Press.

PERELMAN, Chaïm and OLBRECHTS-TYTECA (1989), L., *Tratado de la argumentación. La nueva retórica*, Madrid, Gredos.

RAICHVARG, Daniel y JACQUES, Jean (1991), *Savants et ignorants. Une histoire de la vulgarisation des sciences*, París, Seuil.

VALE, Eugene (1992), *Técnicas del guión para cine y televisión*, Barcelona, Gedisa.

WILLEMS, Jaap and GÖPFERT, Winfried (2006), *Science and the Power of TV*, Amsterdam, VU University Press and Da Vinci Institute.

INDEX